The Sustainab
Smallholders'
Handbook

First published in Great Britain 2019 by
Posthouse Publishing Ltd, No 2 Cleat, St Margaret's Hope, South Ronaldsay, Orkney, KW17 2RW

A CIP catalogue for this book is available from the British Library
ISBN 978 1 903872 33 8

10 9 8 7 6 5 4 3 2 1

The author's sincere thanks go to all who contributed, especially the generous people who agreed to be interviewed for the case studies; Joanne Ainscough; Gary Cairns; Sue Vanstone and the staff at The Rural Business School; all at Downsizer.net; Rod Haselden; Cheryl Arvidson-Keating; Chrissie Davies; Bruce Ross-Smith; Sally Harvey; Ryan Strong; and last but most definitely not least John Turnbull.

Printed and bound in Great Britain by Short Run Press Ltd.

The Sustainable Smallholders' Handbook

A practical guide to living off the land

Lorraine Turnbull

Contents

Author's preface

This book was inspired by the many students I have taught how to manage a smallholding. They came from a variety of backgrounds and ranged in age from their mid-20s to mid-70s. Some were existing smallholders who wanted to learn a particular skill and some were aspiring smallholders who wanted to get a feel for it and decide if it really was for them. Some have gone on to become firm friends; some we never heard from again.

After a full day's course, whether it was tractor servicing, agricultural welding, beekeeping, orchard pruning, lambing or cider-making, there was always that final wistful question while standing looking over the orchard with a cup of tea or glass of cider: "How do you make enough money to live?" As I've answered this question more times than I care to remember with the words, "how long have you got?", I decided to put a book together explaining how we made our tiny smallholding into a profitable business and how we beat the planning system to lift our Agricultural Occupancy Condition.

I have drawn on my experience as a smallholder and as a Training Co-ordinator for The Rural Business School, where one of my duties was to set up suitable events for existing and hopeful smallholders and rural entrepreneurs that have included contributions from friends and acquaintances who run successful rural businesses, many of them smallholdings. Whether you are still at the dreaming stage; are about to take the plunge; or are already a smallholder, this book will explore lots of different options of how to make a profit on your smallholding.

There are lots of different ideas in this book because every situation is different, but there are a range of business ideas and projects to suit most smallholdings and most individuals. This book does not give you a recipe to make your situation and business work; rather I encourage you to cherry-pick ideas depending on your needs, location and budget; but by spreading the risk, working seasonally and concentrating on high value produce and services, you stand a better chance of making a profit while living the good life. With some realistic planning, some learning and a lot of hard work you can run a rural business that supports you financially while allowing you to live the dream.

Many prospective and current smallholders have also asked me how they can live with and even better lift an Agricultural Occupancy Condition (AOC). Sadly, this book is unable to cover either the practices that can be interpreted as fulfilling an AOC or the process involved in lifting an AOC or gaining a Certificate of Existing Lawful Use or Development (CLEUD). Both are possible with the right research and support, and at the very least I would recommend the services of a tried and tested rural property expert in this field. Avoid companies who offer a 'no win-no fee service'; you are only going to get one bite at doing it.

Finally, I can only say that my whole experience of smallholding life was thoroughly worth it. Yes, there were dark, lean days and some awful experiences, but these were balanced by incredible, fulfilling and joyous experiences and I can thoroughly recommend it. Life is for living, and I have some fantastic memories of living the good life.

Lorraine Turnbull
May 2019

Size isn't everything

01

Case Studies

Smallholdings come in all shapes and sizes. Some include dwelling houses; others are just plots of undeveloped land. Some are not really smallholdings at all but houses with large gardens (with or without an allotment!) or even small farms of up to 50 acres; in fact they're as diverse as the people who want to live in and on them.

It goes without saying that you're reading this book because the whole subject fascinates you. Perhaps you're fed up with the rat-race and have an idyllic vision of a self-sufficient life in the countryside. Perhaps you've reached that time of life when you have a bit put by and can live a dream you've nurtured for years. Or perhaps you already have a smallholding and are looking for ideas to increase its productivity. But whoever you are, this book outlines projects that can be profitable whatever kind of plot you may have.

Smallholding may not be an easy business, but you've every reason to believe that it can be a viable one. The Department for Agriculture, Food and Rural Affairs statistics on UK farm income show that small specialised farms raising rare-breed livestock or growing niche horticultural crops make more profit than monocultural cereal prairies, farms with great herds of livestock or large mixed farms, which in 2013-14 relied on state subsidies for a third of their income. In fact 60% of Britain's cereal farms actually made an operating loss! It's the same elsewhere: a 1999 US policy brief indicated that farms of less than 27 acres netted significantly higher returns than larger ones. Many British smallholders have far less land than this and have still established successful businesses; and according to the Institute for Food and Development Policy the small farm's greater profitability is mainly due to specialising in higher-value goods. The message is clear: quality counts.

Today, with the prospect of Brexit looming, the whole question of farm subsidies will soon be up in the air and there is a strong argument to be made for weaning agriculture off subsidies altogether. Many commentators believe that there is a viable place in British agriculture for smaller, more sustainable farms and smallholdings turning out high-quality added-value products intended for carefully targeted markets. Find an authoritative view of the financial future of small-scale farming and the risks and opportunities it faces at **sustainablefoodtrust.org/articles/funding-future-farms/**.

But it's important when considering overall profitability to recognise that smallholding is not concerned solely with food production, and that the category embraces not only a wide variety of types of premises – crofts; former farm labourers' cottages with allotment-sized parcels of land; old rectories and the like with sizeable gardens; houses subject to that little known British institution, the Agricultural Occupancy Restriction (of which much more later); and less permanent New Age caravans, yurts and communes dependent to various extents on their own produce – but also an equally wide range of business activities. Smallholding isn't defined by the type of property in question as much as the operations carried out there. And whether you have one acre or 50, you can make a profit from smallholding. There is no ideal size for your plot, though. Different guides to self-sufficiency and smallholding will suggest an acre or five acres or even 10 acres, but success isn't tied to size. Each individual piece of land will be suited to particular uses – we even explore in this book the very new idea of seaweed cultivation, which is an interesting niche option for smallholders in coastal areas with clean water and insufficient land for more conventional crops – and the people working it will be successful or not according to their practical skills, business acumen and breadth of imagination.

Whatever the potential, though, generating an income from the land is no walk in the park; and you might think it would be even harder to run a fully commercial organic holding and follow a sustainable way of life than to run a conventional farm. But the rewards can more than offset the initial hard graft and set-up costs, especially if you have more than one product or service to offer both to augment the holding's income and to spread the risks.

Spreading your risk will maximise your chances of success. Every enterprise will have its own strengths, but having a number of money-making products or services will cushion failure in other areas. If you rely on a single product or a single big customer, you really have put all your eggs in one basket. Spreading the risk across several products and / or several customers will make your business more resilient and will generate income during the leaner months too. For example, the main income streams at our smallholding in Cornwall were letting a spare room, making and selling cider and servicing garden machinery. I also taught one-day workshops, and we sold surplus garden produce, hatching eggs, and apple trees, rootstocks and scions. This strategy was the result of a conscious decision. When we first moved to our single acre in Cornwall it seemed huge to us. What could we do with all that land? Within a year we were coveting the six-acre field next door. But instead of expanding we cut our coat according to the cloth we had, agreeing to make the best possible use of our one acre and to increase our income with niche products and services that no-one else provided locally. That meant that we were both able to work part-time, supporting two children and running two vehicles while building up our businesses on the smallholding. We worked hard, but we ate well; our kids were brought up in the countryside and we lived a lifestyle we thoroughly enjoyed. Had we been a little younger the additional land might have been useful for us, but we wanted to keep control of what we did and not be overwhelmed by a business that would outgrow us and be no fun at all. We are all individuals, and for us the lifestyle was the important factor.

Family matters

Which brings us to the next big question. You desperately want to live the dream. But is the dream yours alone, or do you share it with your partner and or children?

Honesty is a wonderful thing, and the minute you start planning in earnest to up sticks, move to the country and start yogurt knitting for a living cracks may appear in your family. My husband, for example, was happy with the idea. He's a quiet chap from a farming background who likes a bit of space round him. He's a blacksmith by trade, as was his father, and he loves the country life. The older of my two children, by contrast, was horrified. She was leaving her friends and busy social life to move to Bumpkin Central! The world was going to end. Meanwhile the younger child was busy fantasising about quad bikes and killing things with axes, and my mother couldn't believe that her daughter was going to become… an agricultural labourer!

Some 12 years later and both children are at university. Neither of them plans to work in agriculture, although the younger is very keen on renewables and sustainability. Hopefully they will look back and remember the good times as well as the hard work that made our life on our smallholding. They certainly won't have any illusions about the world owing them a living!

Before you start trawling the internet for smallholdings for sale, therefore, let's pop the kettle on and have a wee chat, just between us. There are some difficult subjects we need to look at.

What is your motivation? Is smallholding something you've always wanted to do? Do you come from a farming background? Are you physically fit and able? Have you any experience with livestock and in the event, could you personally kill an animal? Are you considering a simpler, cheaper way of life because you're struggling in your current situation? In the latter case, understand that working at any level in agriculture or horticulture is no Utopia. Smallholding life is 24/7. Even the most organised, dedicated smallholders will tell you the days are long and that you still have to get out there and work in rain, hail, sleet and snow. We didn't get a family holiday until our eighth year on the smallholding, and it had to be planned like a military exercise. Weekends to do stuff with the children were difficult, which made us unpopular as well as exhausted. Christmas Day is a working day, and your social life revolves round farmers' markets and auctions. The weather and the hours of daylight pretty well govern your days. Cutting the cover off our polytunnel at 3am in a ferocious gale to save the metal structure has to be one of the highlights of 2009.

We've touched briefly on the topic of children, but reconciling their demands with those of the holding is a very thorny subject. Taking on a smallholding while you still have children means a double load of first-priority commitments. Think deeply and seriously about this one: can you cope with both? Children under the age of six will require you to stop and start your chores and work around them, unless you have a very understanding extended family nearby or can afford childcare. Children from 6-12 mean at the very least that you'll have to do school runs, although if you train them to be sensible they will happily amuse themselves outside school hours running through the fields, playing with the livestock and getting thoroughly filthy. Then as they enter teenage years you will, like mums and dads everywhere, become a taxi service; but you'll find your parental minicabbing duties harder than parents in more regular jobs because you'll be keeping track of where the kids are, who they're with and what they're up to while you're lambing, or fixing a fence that the livestock have broken through, or unblocking the overflow from the septic tank. Finally, children will drain your financial resources like a running tap, as they do universally; but the seasonal nature of your income could create problems other parents don't have. And here's another problem that other mothers don't have. Working alone all day in all weathers doing hard, dirty jobs can be very demoralising and lonely but also absorbing. I remember when the kids were at primary school, I had been chopping logs all day and lost track of the time and had to hurry to school to collect them in dirty work clothes and with twigs and spiders in my hair. I can still remember the stares from some of the yummy mummies who obviously thought the school run was a fashion parade and my embarrassed children asking why couldn't I just be normal.

On the other hand, it's not all work and muck: we have enjoyed sun-filled days watching the ducks mess about in their pond, passed evenings outside in sleeping bags watching meteors and the Milky Way and spent many an hour in the orchard watching and listening to the bees rumbling away in a cloud of pink and white petals. We have made some marvellous friends and know we can call on for help and vice versa, and enjoyed the whole experience of smallholding life.

So remember before taking the plunge that this is a big decision for everyone, and life will be much easier if you can all sit down together and have a rational and honest discussion. Imagine that you're presenting a business plan. Have all the facts and figures to show that the family won't be reduced to penury. After all, you will need all the practical and emotional support you can get, so having your family on board is really important. And if you have a partner who is happiest in front of the television or who screams every time a spider appears in the house, then perhaps you seriously need to think whether this is for them. I cannot stress this strongly enough, because one of the major reasons for failures in rural businesses is family relationship problems. If you think living and working together in a physical and demanding rural or land-based business will bring you closer together then think again. If there are any cracks in your relationship to start with, then the monotonous long hours and isolation that can be rural life will magnify them. You need a steady and strong relationship to start with. Remember that both parties have to get something out of the deal, otherwise there is no incentive to stay. Dreaming is all well and good, but it doesn't get the job done and will soon sicken your partner if you do all the dreaming and they do all the work.

If, however, you are in a relationship where you can sit down and listen to each other you will have a partnership that will survive anything. If some project isn't working then you must say so and decide together how to move on. We carried on a small plant nursery business for three years, trying to make it profitable while John worked off the holding to bring in money. Many factors contributed to the failure – poor weather for two summers, recession and the fact that people shop for plants at chain stores. Facing reality and changing tack was not the end of a dream but a step in the right direction. It's better to stop doing something that isn't working and try something else; and this book is about looking at lots of options, some of which will work for you and some that won't.

Relevant experience is another necessary precursor of taking the plunge: how do you know what the job entails and whether you're up to it if you've never tried? If you have no experience at all of country life I would suggest taking the family to visit an Open Farm Sunday **https://farmsunday.org** and gauging their reactions. Open Farm Sundays are held every June on farms all over the UK. Or have a holiday on a working farm: Farm Stay UK **www.farmstay.co.uk** offers B&B, self catering, camping and glamping breaks at different types of farms where you can try your hand at lambing, milking, feeding the pigs and so on and take the opportunity to talk to real live farmers. If you have no children in tow I would suggest volunteering at different times of the year on different types of farm to get a balanced experience of the highs and lows of the seasonal cycle and of the great variety of ways in which all sorts of enterprises are run. A week spent lambing in the Dales sounds idyllic, but your third 12-hour nightshift dealing with difficult births (and deaths), tired and irritable farmers, cold, aches and pains and the solitude may be enough for you to decide that keeping sheep isn't for you!

Planning and finance

The ins and outs of various kinds of property holding are discussed in the next chapter, but even if you aren't going to need a mortgage or much in the way of capital equipment you're definitely going to need a float, and probably a big one. Starting capital typically comes from a house sale, a redundancy cheque and or a bequest, but getting a new business up and running with a positive cashflow from which you can pay yourself doesn't happen overnight, and you will need either contingency funds or an off-site job to live on while you get the ball rolling.

You need to budget not only for general living expenses but also for council tax; course fees if you're training; insurance; building alterations if necessary; transport; animal feed; vets' bills; utilities and domestic expenses and a million other things. A substantial emergency fund is always a good idea, too, especially if your business requires mechanical equipment and you're not much of a mechanic yourself. Even if you plan to live in a caravan or camper van, it all has to be paid for. Having a guaranteed income from an off-site job will not only help you get started, it's also a great fallback if things don't go as planned. So consider a part-time supplementary income for one or both of you, preferably based on the experience you've gained in a previous career. I was able to land a well-paid, interesting part-time job at a nearby agricultural college, which meant I had access to further training as well as an income that allowed John to get his machinery servicing business established. By looking critically at your own skills you're almost bound to find some service you can offer, whether it is book-keeping (always in demand among farmers!), social media, welding (very much in demand) or machinery repair. When I was a bit younger I used to offer lambing help and regularly managed to find a couple of days' work a week over the eight weeks in February and March when I would be not really doing a lot else.

Luckily for us, Cornwall is one of the poorest counties in England and has therefore benefited greatly from EU funding intended to encourage agricultural businesses to diversify. Training was subsidised to a great extent and we took advantage both to update our skills and to boost our income as occasional tutors. And although Britain is about to leave the EU, it seems there will still be funding available in various forms both for training and capital investment. Currently, there is support for new entrants and for farmers below the age of 40 under the EU's Basic Payment Scheme and there is also funding for qualifying small rural business through Defra's LEADER programme. This is quite wide-ranging in its remit: for example a smallholding with an established orchard successfully applied for grant-funding for a press to produce juice and cider. LEADER funding is administered by Local Action Groups: visit **www.leader-programme.org.uk** to find yours. The whole question of government and other support is subject to such sudden and radical change, though, that to pick up on new opportunities and head off new threats you need to keep yourself well-informed. Surf the net, read the trade press and join relevant societies and associations. If you do find funding that you want to apply for, give yourself plenty of time and ideally find someone who has successfully applied before to help you – there is usually a right way and a wrong way to complete the application!

Meanwhile, start drawing up a detailed business plan: you will need to produce one when applying for most funding, and it's a good exercise to do to see exactly how the figures stack up. As noted above, you need a minutely detailed forecast of your monthly and other outgoings: leave nothing out. It will be harder to be equally realistic, however, when you make the corresponding forecast of your income. For instance, I used to keep a flock of 60 hens and 14 ducks to provide eggs to sell either at the gate or to our local shop. The eggs were always popular and sold as soon as they were on the shelf. But after a hard look at the costs, I quickly realised that unless I kept at least 300 chickens the flock was not going to pay. When I deducted my costs from the price the shop paid I was barely covering my labour, let alone all the other expenses. The cost of producing a dozen eggs at time of writing is roughly £2 including hatching, rearing, feed, housing, worming, treating, fencing, packing, labelling and labour. Eggs were and are a low-value product and between these costs and the retail price there wasn't enough room for both farmer and shopkeeper to make a profit.

Then a chance look at an internet auction site revealed that by selling hatching eggs from good pure-breed stock I could make up to 30 times as much for the same number of eggs. So I got rid of my hybrid hens and built up my pens of rare-breed chickens instead to supply hatching eggs; we either ate or sold at the farm gate any that failed to sell. And there are two morals from this story. The first is that a ruthlessly brutal approach to business planning can starkly expose the weak points in your proposed MO, and the second is that small businesses like yours thrive on quality and added value, not on commodities.

The farming tax regime

One column in your business plan will be headed "tax", and to fill this in you will undoubtedly need the help of a specialist accountant. Farming has a very different tax regime from other areas of business and while some of it is fairly straightforward, some is fiendishly difficult to understand and calls for expert advice.

One item of expense you can cross off straight away is business rates for land in agricultural or horticultural use, including forestry. It's exempt, and so are any buildings required to process your produce. Your home, though, will be valued for council tax as normal.

You are allowed a rebate on the duty – and hence a reduction in the VAT – on the diesel you use to power agricultural, horticultura or forestry equipment from chainsaws right up to bulldozers. You may not, however, use red diesel for transportation any further than 1.5km from the farm. The detailed rules – and penalties! – will be explained by the garage or agricultural engineer you buy your red diesel from.

There are complicated exemptions from inheritance tax and Capital Gains Tax (CGT) known as Agricultural Property Reliefs that need not detain us here, although CGT relief will form part of your exit strategy when you want to retire or if you fancy a change of lifestyle.

As a smallholder you'll probably be self-employed. On the one hand, the buck stops with you: no sick or holiday pay, and the bills will continue to drop on the doormat. On the other hand, the National Insurance regime is less onerous and the amount of deductions and allowances you can claim against income tax will reduce it virtually to zero. Only under very rare circumstances will your accountant advise you to set up a limited company; for more general advice on self-employment, visit **www.gov.uk/topic/business-tax/self-employed**.

Claim every benefit, grant or subsidy going. If it hadn't been for Tax Credits we would have had to give up our way of life in the third year. They are being gradually phased out and replaced by Universal Credit, which is much harder to claim and pays a lot less. It may still be worth a couple of hours' form-filling, though:

Case study
Leadketty Farm, Dunning, Perthshire
www.leadkettyfarm.co.uk

Proof if proof were needed that size isn't everything, Leadketty Farm is a long-established smallholding whose 40 acres in the centre of the main soft fruit-growing region of eastern Scotland support an astonishing 140 seasonal workers for six months of the year.

French producers routinely refer to a farm or vineyard's "terroir": the unique interplay of location, aspect, climate and soil that give the produce its distinct identity. Eastern Scotland can claim its own terroir, with loamy soils that heat up quickly, a short growing season but long summer daylight hours and a dry climate quite unlike the west coast's. Thanks to protected cropping, low-cost LED lighting and the propagation of earlier and later varieties, the soft fruit season now runs for a good 20 weeks between May and October. Nationally, demand for quality home-produced soft fruit is increasing, and production has kept up with a 36% increase between 2010 and 2015.

The Corrigalls have been farming here for 80 years and switched from growing potatoes to soft fruit many years ago. They now cultivate 35 acres of strawberries (Sonata and Elsanta) under polytunnels as well as five acres of raspberries (Cascade Delight). They produce an average of 250 tonnes of fruit a year, most of which is distributed by Kentish Garden, a cooperative that supplies all the major supermarket chains with fresh fruit. The Corrigalls have embraced the Red Tractor marketing scheme, and also sell around 10% of their fruit to local shops, restaurants and hotels.

The seasonal workers who spend their summers here come mainly from Eastern Europe, although their numbers are boosted at the height of the season by university students. Full-time staff need to be able to communicate in Polish, Russian, Bulgarian, Latvian and Lithuanian enough to induct the migrants in routines, hygiene, grading and quality control. They are housed on site in caravans with up to six sharing, and are charged for accommodation and electricity. They work a 39-hour week at minimum wage and aim for an average pick rate of 5-10kg an hour. Each worker is given a seven-day trial, after which sub-standard pickers are let go. As with any agricultural business that relies on seasonal migrant labour, the situation post-Brexit is high on the Corrigalls' list of anxieties.

Table-top production is more favoured these days than ground-growing. The strawberries are grown in suspended grow-bags filled with coir for good water retention and watered by automatic irrigation. The height allows for multiple layers and much easier hand-picking and is therefore more productive. Pollination inside the tunnels is provided by mobile mini-hives of bumblebees, which are active on cloudy cold days when honeybees wouldn't leave the hive. They are also more efficient pollinators and don't have the honeybee's urge to migrate. A mobile hive contains around 100 workers and will pollinate for 6-8 weeks.

Soft fruit production is a good bet for smallholders as the crops are high value and in great demand from supermarkets, jam producers and the catering and hospitality trades. Although it's more intensive and perhaps too close to monoculture for many smallholders to feel comfortable with, Leadketty Farm does at least prove that a smallholding can support a significant and thriving business even on a small acreage.

try it and see. Finally, there are government-backed advice centres that can help you decide if setting up a business is right for you. For England see **www.greatbusiness.gov.uk**; for Scotland **www.business.scotland.gov.uk**; for Wales **www.businesswales.gov.wales**; for Northern Ireland **www.investni.com/support-for-business**.

VAT

Seriously consider registering for VAT, even if you're a food business or your annual turnover is below the current threshold of £85,000. But as food is zero-rated and will surely remain so even after Brexit, why let yourself in for hours of extra book-keeping?

There's one excellent reason: it will get you 20 per cent of your capital outlay back. Most start-ups cost a lot in capital investment, and if you're registered the VAT is reclaimable. It's that simple. Hindsight is a wonderful thing: I wish we'd been VAT-registered when we started smallholding. As for the admin, you have to keep books anyway, and there are plenty of online software systems that can manage your VAT and even do your returns for you.

Basic Single Payment

The Basic Single Payment scheme (BSP) is the official name of the EU farm subsidy. Anyone who works 12 acres or more of grazing and or arable is eligible to claim and many smallholders – more than would care to admit it, actually – derive a large part of their income from it. We can only guess at the system that will replace it once we have left the EU but surely it must be simpler: Defra's PDF setting out the terms and conditions of the existing EU scheme runs to 84 pages!

Actually it's neither that difficult to grasp nor that difficult to comply with: it's just that there's so much of it. Check before you exchange contracts or sign a lease to confirm whether the existing entitlement to BSP is being transferred to you. If so, make sure you're registered with the Rural Payments Agency (**www.gov.uk/government/organisations/rural-payments-agency**). The BSP is not only a source of income: many lenders also regard eligibility as security against which funds for investment can be borrowed.

Countryside stewardship

An important source of help in improving your land is the Countryside Stewardship scheme administered by Natural England and its equivalents. Quite significant amounts are available in one-off grants and ongoing subsidies for small but cumulatively expensive improvements to hedges, fences, woodland, flood management, wildlife habitat and biodiversity, run-off control, preserving historic features and many other aspects of land management. The scheme's first purpose is to serve the natural environment, but in the process it can help you with surprisingly generous contributions towards activities such as tree-planting and vermin control that make a solid financial contribution to your holding's productivity.

The drawback's in the bureaucracy, as always: because grants of this nature are inevitably assessed on a case-by-case basis you'll find yourself answering a lot of questions and filling in a lot of forms. But then form-filling of one sort or another is something you'll get used to as a smallholder! It is not unknown for mischievous applicants to cut corners by copying and pasting their neighbour's application; but do remember that the magistrates regard making a false declaration as more than just corner-cutting: it's also a criminal offence. See more at **www.gov.uk/countryside-stewardship-grants** and do give it a good read: the scheme covers so much ground that there's almost bound to be something in there you can benefit from.

Time management

Time management may not form part of your business plan, but it's every bit as important as money management: running out of time can be as catastrophic as running out of money. It's therefore very important when setting up a new business or making major changes to your existing one to scrutinise your time management as closely as you scrutinise your cash flow.

Using a visual aid will help you greatly. A straightforward office holiday planner or variant, using magic markers of different colours to tell you what you should be doing and when, will highlight when you're likely to be overstretched and perhaps in need of more hands to manage all the work – lambing and picking are obvious examples – and will also reveal when you're underemployed and can take on some additional work: winter in particular is a lean time for some kinds of land-based business, and it's the ideal opportunity to catch up with your own book-keeping just in time for the end of the tax year, and perhaps to help (for a fee!) with your neighbours'; update your marketing and social media; and rebuild those important family and social relationships that can get a little lost in the growing season.

The exercise will also show you the amount of time you spend on each activity and give a chance to decide which operations to intensify and which to drop. If the profit you realise from a particular activity is too small for the time and effort you invest in it, then perhaps it's time to assess whether it's worth carrying on with.

Rationalising and monetising your labour will also, perhaps paradoxically, encourage you to stop and just enjoy what you're doing. After all, part of the attraction of smallholding is cherishing those all-important moments of watching lambs gambolling in the paddock or the mating flights of the butterflies, or just sitting with a pint of your own cider with a mate in the orchard discussing the performance of the local football team. Those moments become even more precious when you know how much they're worth and always remember: you're not living to work, you're working to live.

Coping with setbacks

When we moved on to our smallholding, we set out as a small ornamental plant nursery. We had half an acre suited to intensive cultivation and my background was horticulture. Our main income came from John's day-job, which at the time we thought would be temporary while the nursery business grew.

Unfortunately, we had two very wet springs and summers, and then the deepest recession in the UK since WWII (according to the internet) in 2008–09. The weather continued to fail us, and my mother was diagnosed with Alzheimer's and moved in with us. As a small nursery, I couldn't compete with garden centres selling cheap plants imported from the Netherlands. We were one of eight small plant producers in the area that all stopped production within a year or so of each other.

But we didn't just sit there and wait for the bailiffs. We realised we needed a drastic change of direction, so we built on the skills we already had and tailored them to meet local demand. I retrained as a teacher and got part-time work at a local agricultural college while starting to develop a small cider business. John took the plunge to become self-employed and after a very nervous start was soon running a successful garden machinery maintenance business. By facing the situation calmly, we managed to turn a depressing situation round and we never looked back.

We got on top of things before the situation spiralled out of control, but not everyone who encounters such a setback is so fortunate. Farming at any level can be very isolating, and if it all starts to wrong the pressures you can deal with in good times can become impossible to bear. The endless paperwork and the struggle to comply with labyrinthine regulations and demands. The capriciousness of the weather and the unalterable necessity to keep working despite the elements. The apparent impossibility of balancing work and family. The hours of labour for such little reward. Illness, injury, exhaustion. Before you know it you are utterly demoralised and constantly tired. Farming is well-known as one of the worst industries for stress. But it doesn't have to be the end of your dream. If you feel overwhelmed, depressed, lonely or ill, or if you feel it's all starting to fall apart, don't stick your head in the sand and pretend everything is all right.

Seek help. It's all right to take a break, to have a morning off to visit friends if you feel it's all getting a bit much. The farming community understands the stresses of farm life. They understand when weather is poor, animals become sick, crops fail, debts build up and loneliness and isolation start to become an issue. If you are starting to have more bad days than good, then maintain perspective, focus on your positive achievements, take a break, make time to talk and listen and try to identify the problem calmly and rationally.

Even if you haven't built up a supportive network locally, you're not alone. The Farming Community Network (**www.fcn.org.uk**), formerly the Farm Crisis Network, is a voluntary organisation that supports farmers and their families through difficult times. Many of the volunteers are involved in farming or have links with agriculture and understand the issues that farm workers and families regularly face. There's a confidential national helpline (+ 44 (0) 3000 111 999) from 7am–11pm daily, and the FCN can also help with practical business, farm, family and health issues. So don't feel alone; the chances are that someone else has been where you are, and people will listen to you and help you figure out the best course of action.

Top tips for success

Let's not end this chapter on too gloomy a note, though. There will be lean times, of course, but take the following to heart and they'll be few and far between.

- Planning, positivity and patience feature highly in any successful businesses. Make a detailed and realistic business plan, and make sure you all understand the commitment you are making.
- Start small, investing more as profits rise. Try not to borrow: look at grant funding to develop the business. Consider an off-holding paid job – much better than dipping into capital!
- Educate yourselves and listen to other people's experience. You'll make mistakes, but you need to learn from them.

- Horticulture is generally more suited than livestock to low-acreage holdings, and adding value to raw commodities is essential.
- Cultivate local businesses to promote your product as part of their brand ethos.
- Be flexible and be prepared to adapt. Being a multi-tasker is essential.
- Don't rely on one product, but spread the risk by combining a range of enterprises to promote efficiency, especially if by-products can be recycled. Great marketing, high-value niche products and customer care are critical.
- High property prices and the planning system are barriers but not insurmountable. Be very thorough and organised in your approach to planning and grant applications. Be prepared to be rejected and don't be afraid to appeal.

Property and planning

02

The biggest purchase most of us ever make in our lives is a house, and most of us have to take out a mortgage to do it. But getting a mortgage isn't as easy as it used to be, and a steady income and a hefty deposit are both essential. For many start-up smallholders, even those who have the deposit sitting snugly in their banks, the income requirement may be an insuperable obstacle; and with bare agricultural land selling at an average of £6,700 an acre at time of writing (with regional variations), and buildings costing extra, perhaps renting is your best bet. A lot of farms, medium as well as small, are run as long-term tenancies, usually ending with the death or retirement of the tenant. But where to start your search?

Renting

Most but not all private landowners use land agents, who are no more than specialist estate agents, to manage their properties (indeed many land agencies are the dedicated agricultural divisions of ordinary estate agents). Privately rented smallholdings are not all that thick on the ground, and many of them change hands by word of mouth without ever coming on to the open market. Fields and paddocks with road access are particularly prized for equestrianism and tend to be snapped up before outsiders hear about them. If you do find a private rental, though, get professional advice and scrutinise the lease much more closely than you would in the case of a privately rented dwelling: this is, after all, your living as well as your home. You will have to invest money in it, and you want to know well in advance all about issues such as security of tenure and restrictions on use. At the same time, the agents will want to be able to assure their clients that you're competent and know what you're about, that you're solvent, that you aren't going to engage in anything shady or illegal and that the property will be passed back to them in its existing state or better when the tenancy ends.

But land agents need not, and indeed should not, be your first resort. Since the 1890s county councils have owned and leased small farms to provide opportunities for young people to enter agriculture. The initiative really took off after World War I when high death duties (and rather a lot of deaths) meant that there was a lot of surplus land going cheap, returning soldiers to provide for and, thanks to the U-boat scare of 1917, grave concern over the country's food security. Unfortunately many county councils are now selling off their farms to offset cuts in government funding, so opportunities are limited and competition is fierce. Nevertheless, many county councils still own 100 or more small farms specifically intended for new entrants like you, with five or six of them being to let at any one time, so County Hall should be your first stop.

County Councils are not the only public institutions with small parcels of farmland to let. There's the National Trust, of course, and the National Trust for Scotland; and the Royal Society for the Protection of Birds owns more than 200 square kilometres of grazing land on its reserves. Then there are country estates, many of which still have their own administrators and don't use commercial land agents. Many are owned by old families with very deep local roots who not only want their farms to thrive for financial reasons, but also for the continuity of local life and employment. They can be contacted through the Country Land and Business Association (**www.cla.org.uk**), Scottish Land and Estates (**www.scottishlandandestates.co.uk**) or directly through their estate offices.

Finally, crofting may be worth a look. There are more than 20,000 registered crofts in Scotland, around half owned and half tenanted, so perhaps there is an opportunity here for someone who likes the quiet life and can create a self-sufficient lifestyle relatively cheaply. The average size of a croft is five hectares (just over 12 acres), usually of rough pasture only suitable for hill grazing and shooting. It's very difficult to make enough from a croft to support a family, and most crofters have at least one other job. Crofts do come up for sale or let, but there is great demand for them and they are usually only advertised in the local press. Find out more at **www.crofting.scotland.gov.uk** and **www.crofting.org**.

Buying

While renting is the cheaper option, you may feel that it won't really give you the security to establish a profitable long-term business. Investment finance is available for tenant farmers through specialist lenders, but it can be expensive and some lenders specifically exclude start-ups. The same lenders, however, are mostly mortgage providers too: among the many sites to visit for an idea of what you're letting yourself in for if you decide to buy, are **www.ruralmortgages.co.uk**, **www.amconline.co.uk**, and **www.ncfplc.co.uk**.

Gentrification, though, is a major obstacle here. Put simply, any house with enough land to farm commercially, even if it's a run-down 1960s bungalow rather than a quaint Tudor cottage, is worth far more as a dwelling with amenity land than as a smallholding with a dwelling. You may find that you're forced to buy bare land with hope value – i.e., the potential for development somewhere down the line – instead.

Bare land is regularly marketed by land agents, but also privately on the internet and even on internet auction sites. Before you decide to buy bare land as the foundation of your smallholding, though, consider these issues. Off-site housing may be a cheap option, and indeed we have friends who live two miles from their 21-acre holding. They have a few agricultural buildings on site to house their livestock and equipment, and there's an office in one of the buildings with a wood-burner, toilet and kitchen facilities. But security is a major issue, and they have security cameras that can send pictures to their mobile phone. It'll do, just, but as their profits increase they are looking to get permission to build an agricultural dwelling on site.

Getting planning permission to build on agricultural land, however, is fraught with problems, and few people are keen to take it on. The countryside is heavily protected. The 1947 Town and Country Planning Act was designed to prevent overdevelopment and to stop random swathes of housing appearing in the countryside, as had happened in the 1930s; but times have moved on, and the scarcity of building land has forced low-paid rural workers out of their traditional homes to be replaced by more affluent buyers with no interest in agriculture. Here as elsewhere, a toxic combination of gentrification and rigid planning controls has created a housing shortage.

Despite this, planning guidance is constantly changing. Until very recently it was difficult to get permission to convert old farm buildings into dwellings, but over the years a series of measures, the latest only in April 2016 when an amendment to the General Permitted Development Orders came into force, have positively encouraged the adaptation of out-of-date or otherwise redundant farm buildings for new purposes, including residential. Mainly, it must be said, these measures have been intended to enable property developers and large farmers to profit from converting historic or quaint buildings unsuited to modern farming, rather than to help smallholders who only want to find a way of actually living on their land. But at least it is now theoretically possible to turn a ramshackle old shed or a derelict barn into a home. For more detailed information contact Chapter7 on **www.tlio.org.uk/chapter7** and buy its Planning Handbook, a guide to the planning system for smallholders, family farmers, woodsmen, low-impact builders, caravan dwellers and others who want to live and work in the country. Alternatively, find a good planning consultant. You might also keep up with a topical blog, **planninglawblog.blogspot.co.uk**, from Martin Goodall, a solicitor with many years' experience in planning.

Permanent dwelling

What you and your family want, of course, is a snug and secure home on the holding itself. But there's an intermediate stage: in practice the planning authorities may (and probably will) offer you permission for a temporary structure on the site for between two and five years. After that you can apply for permission to build a proper house, although the application will probably have to be supported by proof that the holding is viable. Temporary structures are usually reckoned to be chicken runs and similar buildings with a practical purpose rather than any sort of dwelling, but the definition can be stretched to include a mobile home, a caravan or camper van, a yurt or even an old bus provided its internal space doesn't exceed 10 cubic metres and you can show that it can be moved if required.

To get permission for a permanent dwelling, you need to prove that you are working full-time or at least primarily employed within an agricultural enterprise. You will also need to show that the enterprise has been running as a business for at least three years; that for at least one of those years it made a profit; and that the enterprise is financially viable. You will need to produce a business plan and a professional appraisal of the current and future viability of the business. You may also have to produce your books for inspection, so do get sound professional advice from a specialist surveyor or your accountant before submitting your application.

You will also have to prove that it is essential that someone has to live permanently on site. Security reasons alone are enough; lambing or calving will probably not be enough, as these are temporary or seasonal activities that don't require permanent occupation of the site. Alpaca breeding has been put forward as a business activity that requires continual supervision and therefore permanent residence because alpacas can give birth at any time of day or night and at any time of the year. Owners argue that the alpaca's breeding cycle is so unpredictable that they need to be on site round the clock to catch oestrus at exactly the right moment. One such couple, Bob and Lesley Rawlins, built up a thriving alpaca breeding farm on a six-acre holding: they gained permission for a temporary dwelling on site in 2003, and then permission for a permanent house (albeit with an Agricultural Occupancy Condition or AOC) in 2005, thanks to the success of the business.

AOCs restrict you to agricultural uses for your land, so if you wanted to change it to an amenity use – a riding school or a driving range, say – you couldn't. There is much more on AOCs later, but if you see a holding with or without buildings on the market for significantly less than it ought to command, it may well be subject to an AOC. These type of dwellings are priced at roughly a third less than they would be otherwise because most buyers can't or simply won't accept the concomitant restrictions, and as a result the market for subject properties is much weaker. But don't be led astray by the low price: there is a corresponding problem with raising loans on a subject property, and many mortgage lenders will demand a very substantial deposit. There are other drawbacks to the AOC too, which are significant enough to require examination in a separate appendix.

Searches

Your purchase will be subject to the usual searches before contracts are exchanged, but there are others you will want to make as well whether buying or renting. Are there any public rights of way on the property? Not only is this an issue for the privacy and security of your home and equipment, but if you intend to keep livestock it may also be a biosecurity and animal welfare problem. You can view Ordnance Survey maps that show up-to-date public footpaths and bridle paths free online at **www.ordnancesurvey.cu.uk**, but you will need to walk the land yourself to assess issues such as vehicle access to fields; width and condition of paths and gates; state of hedges, fence and ditches; swampy patches; tree cover and other variables you won't find on a map.

Are there any restrictive covenants on the land? Common covenants include not causing any nuisance to neighbours, not keeping livestock and not carrying on a business at the property. Any of these would jeopardise or even kill the idea of smallholding on the land stone dead, but it would be a neglectful solicitor indeed who didn't flag them up well in advance. You will need legal advice, but covenants can be overturned by applying to the Upper Tribunal (Lands Chamber) for discharge or modification of land affected by a restrictive covenant. Find more information here: **www.gov.uk/courts-tribunals/upper-tribunal-lands-chamber**.

Assessing a plot

Where people choose to settle is usually determined by external factors such as family ties and other local connections. But some are footloose and fancy-free and can hunt for suitable holdings wherever they feel drawn to, whether by hard-headed considerations such as likely return on capital or by personal preferences such as a yearning for the sea or a love of the Highlands.

Most of us are probably pretty familiar with climatic conditions in different parts of Great Britain: western and northern Scotland, north Wales and the hillier parts of the north of England are cold, wet, windy and have soil that is for the most part pretty poor. Land is therefore cheap, especially land that's exposed and badly drained. South Wales, the Welsh border counties and the south-west of England are also wet and windy, prone to flooding and possessed only of pockets of good soil, but land here is more expensive because of competition from amenity and domestic users. The south and east, extending north as far as eastern Scotland, are warmer, drier, better-drained and vastly more expensive. We all know this, but the extent of the variations in economic terms may come as a surprise: the growing season in the extreme north of Scotland is 60 whole days shorter than in the extreme south of England (although of course the summer days are lighter for longer). That doesn't mean that some parts of Scotland – Tayside, to be precise – can't grow some of the best soft fruit in the world, nor that raising indigenous cattle such as Highland Longhorn, the Aberdeen Angus, the Devon Red or the Welsh Black on rough hill pasture can't be highly profitable; it just means that you have to make yourself intimately aware of the circumstances you will face and lay your plans accordingly.

While location is certainly important, you also need to make a very close inspection of the individual features of every plot you view. Hillsides might be open to the sun, sheltered from the prevailing wind, well-drained and thus perfect for apples or vines, but they also tend to have thinner, poorer soil that makes them quite unsuitable for market gardening. Deep valleys can be frost-pockets, lacking sunlight and often waterlogged. Fields surrounded by large established trees may look lush but turn out to be depleted and shady with the soil full of roots. Ask these questions of the vendor or agent at every viewing, and if there's any hint of hesitation or dissimulation, walk away.

Your own eyes, though, will often be all you need to detect any bear-traps, and here are a few to look out for.

- Clumps of rushes and water pooling on the surface indicate poor drainage and possibly clay soil. How much of the plot is affected? Has the land ever been drained? Underground mole drains, clay drain tiles and a perforated water pipe may not be visible, but tell-tale drainage ditches running along field edges may betray a problem with wet soil.
- Alternatively, your problem may be a plot that's too dry. Ideally you want land that's well-drained but fertile, possibly with a small clean stream bordering the fields. In reality, there may not be any running water at all and you'll have to bowser water to your livestock or run waterpipes out to your fields.
- Land that has been abandoned for years may need clearing and reseeding and given time to recover, and land infested with bracken needs expert advice to clear and maintain.
- Windy areas can be recognised even on a calm summer's day by the paucity of trees and the poverty of the hedges, with all the larger vegetation bending away from the prevailing wind. In some such areas even stout windbreaker hedges may be insufficient.
- Coastal land may be sandy and free-draining soil but subject to occasional coastal flooding and salt deposits. Seaweed as a crop will be discussed later, but tourism-based ventures such as camp and caravan sites and holiday letting will probably make more money than attempting to farm, providing you can get planning permission.

Don't just look at the plot you're viewing, either: survey neighbouring fields as far as possible for indicators of what works locally. Checking whether the land is arable (good quality), pasture (medium quality) or rough or subsistence grazing (poor quality) will not only tell you what you might achieve here but is also an indicator of what the price should be. Unfortunately, even small pockets of land unsuitable for modern farming equipment are not likely to come cheap. They are useful for storage, pony keep or for a few pigs; nothing is unwanted land!

And look with more than just your own eyes: a small soil-testing kit costs only a few pounds from agricultural stores and will give you a rough analysis of whether the soil is acid or alkali. For crops, fruit trees and pasture the ideal pH is around 6.5.

One thing to remember is that however unpromising the parcels of land you're viewing might appear to be, there are projects that can work almost anywhere in the UK. In the far north of Scotland, the moors of North Yorkshire, and parts of the south-west, shooting and fishing are big business. Poor soil may be unsuitable for conventional arable crops, but niche crops such as Christmas trees, willow or various species of nut will thrive. And for the last few years, acidic moorland soil has been producing the juniper and other obscure botanicals for the burgeoning artisan gin industry.

Pylons and power lines

So you've viewed various sites and have had a penetrating look at the land. You've made sketches and have maps marking all the relevant features including buildings, walls, hedges, ponds etc. (not forgetting a compass point, of course), and you've made notes of everything you'll need to remember. But one or more amazingly obvious objects might escape your notice simply because we all take them for granted. I'm talking about electricity pylons.

A pylon is an excellent bargaining chip when it comes to negotiating the price of farm property, because for health and safety reasons most farm equipment can't work underneath them. It has even been suggested that the largest pylons might devalue houses within 200m of them by as much as 20 per cent. That's despite the fact that most pylons were sited under annual wayleave agreements (effectively a form of rent) expressly intended to compensate the landowner for loss of the use of the affected land. Most landowners don't seem to realise that they can terminate and renegotiate these agreements, or claim compensation. They can also claim compensation against the smaller 33kV type of wooden pole lines that cross the property. A claim for compensation won't be affected if you were fully aware of the line when you bought the property; or if the property was built after the power line was constructed; or if you are not even contemplating selling the property. However if you have claimed in the past then you will not be eligible to claim again.

Firstly you have to contact your distribution network operator. This is NOT your electricity supplier. There are ten across the UK; you can find them on **www.energynetworks.org**. You can claim directly or employ a no-win no-fee company who will deal with everything for you, normally for a fee of 10-20 per cent if successful. Naturally, they will say that they will negotiate a larger amount of compensation than you could without their help, which may or may not be true. Compensation values depend on the proximity of the pole and wires, and the voltage carried. It can take between six and 18 months to process and requires a surveyors' visit and the appointment of a solicitor, who may be paid for by the electricity company. The process can be time-consuming, but bear in mind that the compensation can range from a few thousand pounds to tens of thousands; and it is certainly worth having a chat with any of the helpful companies vying for your business.

Home and farm security

More than ever these days, security is really important. You will be investing not only in your home and contents but also in machinery and livestock which many criminal gangs regard as comparatively easy pickings. Naturally, you will have insurance, but prevention is so much better than cure.

You already how to check and improve the security of your home.

Case study
Muxbeare Orchard, Willand, Devon

The dream of a sustainable life on a smallholding turned into a four-year planning nightmare for Stig and Dinah Mason when they handed back the keys of their council flat in Baldock, Hertfordshire, and moved into a converted horsebox in a derelict four-acre orchard near Willand, east Devon.

The year was 2009, and a £75,000 bequest from an aunt seemed to be the answer to the couple's prayers. Stig was a stay-at-home dad who had already cut his teeth on chicken-keeping, recycling and handyman skills, but the Masons struggled to get by on Dinah's meagre wage and felt they could offer young sons Dali and Yosse a fuller life on a self-sufficient and sustainable smallholding.

The site they chose seemed ideal. It hadn't been managed for 50 years and apart from overgrown trees the only thing on it was a barn as derelict as the site itself. Unfortunately for the Masons, though, the orchard was only near Willand, not actually in it. Mid-Devon Council ruled that as it was outside the boundary of the nearest settlement it constituted open farmland that they couldn't build on or even live on. Many of the locals were suspicious too, fearing that the unconventional family and its horsebox were the spearhead of an invasion, and that if they were allowed to stay the orchard would soon fill up with nomadic undesirables.

Within a month the council had served an enforcement notice requiring them to leave. Instead, they charmed the locals by involving themselves in the community, and got 1,400 signatures supporting their application to build a straw-bale house in the orchard. The council, though, refused permission and in June 2011 took them to county court where they were threatened with jail if they didn't comply.

They complied. But only for a while. Early in 2012 the government released its new National Planning Policy Framework (NPPF) that substantially modified the previous presumption that piecemeal residential development should not be permitted on agricultural land. The clause that altered the Masons' case, clause 55, states: "Local planning authorities should avoid new isolated homes in the countryside unless there are special circumstances such as:

- the essential need for a rural worker to live permanently at or near their place of work in the countryside; or
- where such development would represent the optimal viable use of a heritage asset or would be appropriate enabling development to secure the future of heritage assets; or
- where the development would re-use redundant or disused buildings and lead to an enhancement to the immediate setting; or
- the exceptional quality or innovative nature of the design of the dwelling."

"Development that is sustainable should go ahead, without delay," wrote planning minister Greg Clark in the preamble to new NPPF. "A presumption in favour of sustainable development is the basis for every plan and every decision." This sudden change of attitude obliged the council to allow the Masons to bring their horsebox back from the traveller site where they had taken refuge and also attracted the attention of Ben Fogle, who featured the family in his Channel 5 series New Lives in the UK. The council still wouldn't allow the straw-bale house but in 2013 approved the (rather more expensive) restoration and conversion of the barn. Stig, Dinah and the boys finally moved in to their new – and almost completely off-grid – home in 2015.

They now run and make their living from what is pretty much the ideal sustainable smallholding. They use solar power, a wood-burning stove and rainwater run-off; they keep pigs, chickens, geese, and bees; they grow vegetables in a polytunnel, medicinal and culinary herbs in Dinah's kitchen garden and apples for both juice and cider in the orchard.

Dinah has set out the family's manifesto as follows:

- To live a sustainable lifestyle whereby we are able to feed ourselves and our family.
- To give back to the local community and surrounding communities.
- To give our children the knowledge of living within the seasons, growing local organic food.
- To look after our children as full-time parents and part-time workers rather than full-time workers and part-time parents.
- To live in a low-impact traditionally built house constructed from natural materials on a smallholding, working with the orchard and growing organic food.

Five objectives: five ticks.

(See the 2012 NPPF in full at **www.gov.uk/publications/national-planning-policy-framework.** You might find it enlightening!)

You have a wander round and try to work out how you'd get in if you left your keys at work or in the pub. Are there open windows? Ladders or garden tools lying around? Do you leave a spare key in the plant pot next to the door or even under the mat? Where do you leave car keys? Where do you keep jewellery, cards, cash? Once you start thinking like a thief, it's pretty easy to see where you can make small changes to secure your property. If you don't, you may be invalidating your insurance. That's upsetting enough when it's the TV and the engagement ring that go. Imagine it's your brand-new tractor.

Now carry out exactly the same exercise in your yard. If a thief can get into your downstairs loo he can definitely get into your tractor shed, because there's no-one close enough to hear the sound of breaking glass. And remember: if you live in town and your security measures thwart a burglar he can easily try elsewhere. Once he's decided to have a crack at your barn, though, he's committed. It's either you or a night of slim pickings.

So fit insurance-approved security locks to all perimeter doors and USE them. Fit and use security locks on all ground and accessible first floor windows. Get an alarm system. Fit heavy-duty padlocks to all outbuildings. Crunching gravel paths and dogs and security lights will alert you to the approach of visitors. Have your dogs microchipped and keep photos and descriptions of them. Pedigree and working dogs have a resale value and even mutts are highly sought after by dog-fighting gangs. Keeping dogs in a yard will alert you to intruders if you are around, but are also easy to poison, whereas a dog inside a farmhouse is harder to silence and is therefore a better deterrent.

Secure ladders and tools out of sight. Install outdoor lighting, and fit a timer to indoor lights for when you're away. Stolen central heating oil is sold as diesel, so make sure your oil tank and your red diesel tank are both secured with heavy-duty padlocks.

Small power tools are easy and quick to steal and resell. Horse tack is another favourite, and more recently the theft to order of rare breed poultry and livestock has also become common. Vintage tractors, trailers and heavy equipment are all highly sought after and take a short time to steal. Mark all machinery, tack and tools with ultraviolet marking to identify it. Keep photographs, descriptions and serial numbers in a safe place.

Remove keys and secure cars, tractors and trailers when unattended. Consider tracking devices, and have the registration numbers etched on vehicle windows. Secure ATVs with chains. Cover the inside of shed windows with old newspaper or opaque security film – it allows a little light in but prevents the opportunist thief from seeing what is inside.

If you have invested in solar power and have ground-mounted solar panels, ensure they are attached with stainless steel bolts with tamper-proof heads. A single pick-up truck could easily take all your solar panels away in an afternoon. Fake or real security cameras may be a deterrent, but you will have to display signs telling visitors that you are filming and the footage may not be admissible in court. Phone your local crime prevention officer to find out.

Keep on friendly terms with your local police. If they know they can pop in for a coffee occasionally, they are more likely to keep an eye on your property. And build similar relationships with nearby farms and neighbours: if they all keep an eye on suspicious activity, it makes rural properties a less inviting option.

Insurance

Anyone with a mortgage has life insurance to pay the outstanding balance if they die, buildings insurance to pay the outstanding balance if the house falls down and contents insurance in case of flood, fire, crime or public insurrection. Everyone in business knows that that's just the start of it.

Perhaps the most important insurance any business should have is Employer's Liability Insurance. This isn't because farming is such a dangerous occupation – although it can be if you're unskilled or incautious – but because the penalty for not having it is £2,500. Per day. Yes, per day. It's not expensive to buy – as little as £30 a year can buy you £5 million in cover, although you'd be well advised to spend £45 and get £10 million. But if you ever hire anybody for any length of time and for any purpose, get EL. If, as is likely, you never employ anyone, get yourself covered against illness and injury. Many a small business has been ruined by the proprietor falling off a ladder or suffering a stress-related coronary, and smallholders are likelier to be found up a ladder or stressing out than most.

Perverse as it seems to many, you also have a duty of care to ramblers, ravers, picnickers, sales reps, Jehovah's Witnesses, hare-coursers, sheep rustlers, tractor thieves, burglars or anybody else, invited or uninvited, who strays on to your land, especially if there are public rights of way (which, by the way, you are not permitted to obstruct or to allow to become overgrown) on your land. But even if your land has no public right of access, you could still be liable for compensation for any injury sustained by someone on your land: the Countryside and Rights of Way Act 2000 gives the 'freedom to roam' on some private land. This means members of the public on your land may slip, trip or fall and then claim from you for their injuries. Third party property damage is another risk you face as a landowner. If a branch falls from a tree on your land and hits a vehicle or person underneath you are responsible. A specialist such as NFU is likely but not guaranteed to offer the cheapest cover.

Just as civilians get pet insurance, so farmers get insurance for the medical care of their livestock; and as, ever since vets discovered that they could get insurance companies to pay them they have ramped up their fees to astronomical heights, this is perhaps the only way you can afford to have your pig dosed. As a food or drink producer you are also advised to have product insurance. A mouse can fall into anyone's loaf or a snail into anyone's bottle of ginger beer, these being two of the most famous food contamination cases in legal history.

Actually, the range of insurances you could have is almost as long as the list of crimes you need to guard against, and if you had every kind of insurance available your cash flow would soon be a cash trickle. But running a business is stressful enough without worrying whether a fire, theft or other crisis is going to stop you trading altogether. There are specialist insurers such as NFU Mutual and brokers such as Towergate who will write you a single policy to cover the whole shooting match, and perhaps that's the best place to start. Just don't be talked into buying any policies you don't need and, as with car insurance, watch that the premiums aren't sneakily doubled at renewal time.

Learning the ropes

03

I have met many successful rural businesspeople and they all have certain things in common. A sense of humour (you need one in this business); a sense of their own worth; a pride in what they do; and the ability to look at situations level-headedly. Every one of them has worked hard and made sacrifices for their success. But if I asked them to define their strengths and weaknesses they would all have a different answer. Some are great at maths, some are terrible at maths. Some have really embraced technology, some are wonderful communicators and terrific with people. They are all human and unique, and there is no single skillset to ensure success.

Personal skills

All of us have some existing skills, whatever background we come from – some of which will undoubtedly prove to be of great practical value. If you've worked with cars or have an engineering background you can probably understand technical manuals and jargon. You might be able to service your own car and change parts. With a little training you could probably service a livestock trailer, possibly even a tractor. Skills like these will not only save you on garage bills, they also mean that not everything grinds to a halt if there's a mechanical breakdown. More than that, they could form the basis of a profitable sideline or even a business in itself servicing petrol-driven motors such as lawnmowers, lawn tractors and other garden machinery. It used to take John roughly an hour to service a push-along petrol mower; slightly longer for a ride-on at a very modest £45 and £100 respectively. My own background was in horticulture. I started gardening at the age of just nine, and as I grew up I enjoyed expanding my knowledge of plants and then of garden design. This led to an RHS Level 3 in horticulture and eventually to a teaching qualification. Even though we decided to give up our plant nursery business, I had built up practical skills and experience on a foundation of theoretical knowledge that was bound to prove useful on a smallholding.

Some smallholders have always worked in the country and are

well-versed in horticulture or agriculture, but many have urban backgrounds and occupations. Their experience can also be really useful, though, so don't discount it. Accountants and ex-bank staff are usually expert in the vital skills of book-keeping, business administration and compliance (see below), while IT professionals have a huge advantage in equally vital areas such as research and marketing. Working out your own strengths and weaknesses is an essential precursor to starting a new life in which you will be, for the most part, on your own, so you can get a good idea of how and whether you'll cope by carrying out a good old-fashioned SWOT analysis (see below)... on yourself. You may feel a little self-conscious, but if undertaken seriously this is a really useful exercise and the resulting document should be kept alongside your business plan. So here we go.

- **S**trengths: What you do well? What are your resources (buildings, equipment etc.)? What support do you have?
- **W**eaknesses: What should you avoid? What do you need training in? What's going to hold you back?
- **O**pportunities: Does your product fit any trends? Is there anything similar to your product on the local market? Will any emergent technology help you?
- **T**hreats: Who is your competition? Are there any changes in the law / technology that will negatively affect your product idea? Are your resources adequate for what you plan to do?

Looking at my own background, I have acquired a mixture of social, technological, technical and horticultural skills. I can organise, communicate, assess risk, do basic accounting and cash flow, manage staff, do first aid, kill humanely, grow plants, manage my own website and social media and teach. My husband is great with machinery. He is a blacksmith by trade but has many other skills. He is a great mechanic, can weld upside down and in all weathers, loves to strip engines down, diagnose faults and then find old engines that he can cannibalise. These skills were very valuable on our holding, but also became a standalone farm machinery repair business.

Make a list of all the existing skills you have and another of things you'd like to brush up on or learn from scratch (as per your SWOT analysis above) and plan how to put them to best use and what to do to correct your deficiencies.

Book-keeping and business administration

A facility for book-keeping and business administration are essential whatever business you're in. You need to know at all times where your money is, what it's doing, whether you're in credit or debit, which customers have paid and who hasn't. Accurate and up-to-date financial records aren't just documents you store up for the annual tax return: they will tell you at any time how healthy your business is. You can use the services of a farm administrator, farm secretary, or accountant; but there's no substitute for knowing your own finances, and of course doing as much as you can without paying a professional saves money.

At first I used to use a simple account book, but in the later years I computerised it using Excel. I wasn't VAT registered, so it was all simple enough. I kept a separate business bank account and did my accounts every two months. I also went on a one-day course at the local tax office. Everyone seems to have a very negative opinion of tax officials, but you can learn the most useful things from them. All they want is to make sure you're paying the right amount of tax and will often, like accountants, point out where you can save money.

A good place to start honing your business administration and book-keeping skills is the Institute of Agricultural Secretaries and Administrators: **www.iagsa.co.uk**. It produces the very useful *Farm Office Handbook* that will tell you all about setting up accounting systems, computerising manual accounts, VAT and payroll for small rural businesses, year-end procedures and statutory and assurance records. Alternatively, you can do a Rural Business Administration Certificate online: the year-long course covers accounts, wages, employment and livestock and crop records **www.bridgwater.ac.uk/course.php?sector=2&subject=30&course=256**.

More general training in office and management skills is readily available at community colleges and through privately-run courses.

Many – such as accounting and setting up a website – can be accessed almost anywhere, often via part-time short courses running one evening a week for up to a year. Some centres also offer intensive courses of perhaps three or four full days over the course of a week. I remember many years ago attending a business start-up week. Every day we took a bite-sized training session in a different topic, and one day we examined setting up a simple manual book-keeping system. I continued to use it until a couple of years ago when I moved the same simple system over to the computer. I like the simplicity, but the computer does the sums now and is far quicker and more accurate than I ever was! Another day covered basic marketing. Points covered included choosing a name, marketing methods and monitoring customer response. These days, a good website and other social media presence with lots of professional-quality photography and videos are a must – pictures really are worth a thousand words. Google your community college or local government adult education service for syllabuses. Some courses may be funded depending on your personal circumstances (and if they're not, the course fees and attendance expenses will be fully tax-deductible), and you may be able to fit in training while still working. My local adult education service offered help with childcare in some circumstances.

General skills

General training is available in a great diversity of formats that have evolved to suit the widely varying requirements of trainees. At one end of the spectrum there are world-leading agricultural universities such as Harper Adams in Shropshire and the Royal at Cirencester where you can get a bachelor's followed by a postgraduate degree in the most abstruse and highly-specialised agriculture-related subjects you can imagine. You don't have to do a formal full-time three-year degree, though: most agricultural colleges offer a variety, including full-time, block-release and day-release courses leading to many different certificates and qualifications. Visit **www.aoc.co.uk/land-based-colleges**.

At the other end of the spectrum you can educate yourself through books and magazines at every level of specificity and difficulty, as well as online videos and fully certificated home-learning courses. You can put flesh on the bones of your reading through the many less formal hands-on courses in severely practical subjects such as animal handling, pruning, welding beekeeping, pig keeping, pig butchery and so forth, many of them offered by fellow-smallholders earning a little extra by handing on their own specialisms – which you can do yourself, of course (see Chapter 8). But do look for an experienced trainer with the appropriate insurance and first-hand personal endorsements. There are also many crafts that of necessity have to be located in rural settings. Blacksmithing and charcoal making are two examples. Other rural businesses may include animal boarding, growing Christmas trees, firewood production, bottling spring water, tanning and composting. Training in these less common areas is hard to find, but joining a local smallholders group or club is a good start. In Devon, for example, DASH **www.devonssmallholders.co.uk** is run by the members and has a dedicated training section. As a paid-up member you can take advantage of discounted training run by very experienced people: a day-long introduction to pig keeping, for instance, costs £50 (at time of writing) and covers regulations, choosing the right breed, managing the land, fencing, housing and feeding and includes a hands-on practical session. This is only one of a whole range of courses on offer, and there are similar associations, groups and clubs all over the UK.

Somewhere between agricultural universities and peer-to-peer practical training there are full and part-time courses at Colleges of Further and Higher Education across the country some of which are world leaders in their fields: Plumpton in Sussex, for example, specialises in viticulture and oenology. Rural skills training is also offered in association with colleges by organisations such as Lantra. Lantra (it's short for Land Training) is a provider of industry-recognised qualifications in a range of rural skills including agriculture, horticulture, forestry, health and safety, animal health and machinery: **www.lantra.co.uk**.

If you're considering a project involving potentially dangerous machinery, chemicals or trees then remember that many insurance firms will insist that you have appropriate and up-to-date certification. Community centres in rural areas often run first aid courses and personally I'd suggest that first aid training should be essential if you're carrying on a high-risk business in an isolated location – even more so if you are going to have volunteers and or visitors on site.

Specialised training

Specialised training in (sometimes literally) the nuts and bolts of the business is often best provided, as we saw above, by fellow smallholders who generate additional revenue by sharing their wisdom with neophytes, and whose number you may very well join one day. Sometimes private trainers are the only way you can access training of this sort, and you may very well find that if it's in-depth training in a specific craft that you're after, you have to go to several platforms to acquire it.

To choose an example of which I have personal experience, if you want to set up a small-scale cidermaking enterprise, you will need a thorough operating knowledge of:

- Arboriculture and orchard management
- The cidermaking process itself
- Liquor licensing, excise duty, planning, and compliance issues
- Marketing and social media
- Book-keeping and business administration

No single centre in Britain offers a course with all these as modules. Shuttleworth Collge in Bedordshire runs various arboriculture courses, as does Plumpton College. A number of local colleges in the West Midlands – notably Pershore and Hereford and Ludlow – are strong on cidermaking. There are literally hundreds of providers across the country that teach the one-day course required to gain the indispensable personal liquor licence; information on duty, planning and compliance is available on the net; for book-keeping and business administration, see the section above.

Comprehensive single-centre training is available, but only privately. If you decide to go into orcharding and either juicing or cidermaking or both commercially, the Cider and Perry Academy at

Hartpury in Gloucestershire is undoubtedly the country's leading centre. Proprietor Peter Mitchell has been head of the Food and Drink Centre of Regional Excellence at Pershore College, head of production at Hindlip Centre for Cider, and head of department at Worcestershire College of Agriculture. He set up the Orchard Centre when Government funding was withdrawn from Core F&D and today runs a number of intensive courses primarily aimed at commercial makers. I attended two when I was setting up Spotted Dog Cider and found them both very helpful. Visit **www.cider-academy.co.uk**.

If you find the courses a bit light on the orcharding side, Day's Cottage Cider not far away runs orchard and tree management courses, and you may find as a general rule that locally based tuition is the most practical way of picking up the skills you need to cultivate, maintain and crop an orchard. Most parts of the UK and especially the cider apple-growing regions of Herefordshire, Worcestershire, Gloucestershire and the south west have local apple groups. Joining one will give you an opportunity to get very cheap, hands-on training in all aspects of fruit tree growing from planning, planting and pruning the orchard to choosing varieties suitable for your location, pest control, grafting and often juice and cider making on a small scale. Most groups have access to milling and pressing equipment and will often rent it out for a small fee. Having been involved with a couple of these groups in the south west, I can tell you that the wealth of information and knowledge that you can gather from them, together with hands-on experience, is invaluable, and fellow-members are often very knowledgeable about a range of fruit trees other than apples and pears.

Learning as a volunteer

One way of getting intensive hands-on training and practical experience is to volunteer as a helper on an existing smallholding. When I was planning to keep sheep, I volunteered to help friends who ran a flock of 650 with the lambing. The first year they laughed at my efforts, but appreciated my ability to bed up pens, carry water and bottle-feed orphans. The following year I learned more, and eventually they felt confident enough to let me do some shifts on my own. It was a wonderful experience, and I gained the knowledge to deal with my own lambing.

There are organisations such as Worldwide Opportunities on Organic Farms **www.wwoof.org.uk** and HelpX **www.helpx.net** that specialise in matching would-be volunteers to farms and gardens where the host offers bed and board as well as instruction in exchange for your work. If you don't have the time to volunteer long term, then contact your local Young Farmers Club, which ought to be able to find you a suitable placement.

Online learning

There is also, for those too busy to get away from the holding, a wide range of e-learning options, some of which lead to formally recognised qualifications. The Farmers Weekly Academy is a leading name in the field and provides Continuous Professional Development points with a number of accredited bodies such as BASIS and NRoSO (both concerned with safety and other issues related to the storage and handling of agricultural chemicals) and Dairy Pro (self-explanatory!). The Academy has more than 100 modules: visit **www.fwi.c.uk/academy**.

Away from the more formal side of things, the internet is as much a treasure-trove of information for the smallholder as it is for the general user. Short instructional videos on YouTube; dedicated sites on specific areas of agriculture, horticulture and forestry; planning and licensing regulations in the original officialise – if you want it, it's there. Online forums and communities also offer a wealth of knowledge, the Accidental Smallholder (**accidentalsmallholder.net/forum**) and **downsizer.net** being only two. There may be more than one opinion of the best way to do something, but as long as you bear this in mind there are a lot of people out there with a lot of experience who are happy to help and explain things.

Compulsory qualifications

Anyone who uses or applies pesticides in agriculture, horticulture, forestry or amenity workplaces must possess a valid pesticide certificate. This applies whether you are self-employed, an employee or a volunteer. The foundation module, PA1, has to be passed before you can take any other modules (PA2-PA6). There is no longer an exemption in UK law commonly known as 'grandfather rights', which expired in 2015.

Any employee or volunteer required to use a chainsaw must be able to show a valid 'ticket' – i.e., a City and Guilds certificate of competence. You yourself don't need one, although the short course involved is useful in itself and your insurance company might require it.

If you have a full driving license issued on or after 1 January 1997 you can legally drive a van of up to 3.5 tonnes maximum authorised mass (MAM) towing a trailer of up to 750kg MAM; and you can tow a trailer over 750kg MAM as long as the combined MAM of the towing vehicle and the trailer is no more than 3,500kg. The MAM is the maximum weight when loaded (i.e. with cattle, pigs, feed etc AND occupants AND fuel). If you want to tow anything heavier you have to pass the car and trailer driving test **www.gov.uk/car-trailer-driving-test**. The test lasts roughly an hour and is based on the LGV lorry test. It must be paid for when booked and at time of writing costs £115. However, if you passed your test before 1997, check your licence for entitlement to drive a vehicle and trailer of up to 8,250kg MAM. This should be shown in section 9 of the new photocard license; categories BE, C1, and C1E (with restrictions on this last category). So you don't have to sit a special test; although you may want a little tuition in driving with a trailer if you have never done it, especially reversing.

Drivers and attendants using road vehicles to transport farm animals, horses, or birds in connection with an economic activity (i.e. a farm business) for distances exceeding 65km also require an animal transport certificate of competence (ATC). There are many centres that offer the qualification including most, if not all, agricultural colleges. Anything bigger than a goose really needs a trailer of some sort, but chickens, ducks and geese can be transported in cardboard boxes or special carriers.

Livestock regulations and management

04

For many, the sole reason for seeking a life in the country with a patch of land to call their own is that they want to keep livestock. They may have had a lifelong hankering for chickens or donkeys or they may feel that the traditional country way of life necessarily implies keeping a couple of pigs. It's harder to make money from animals than it is from fruit and vegetables and there are smallholdings that keep no livestock at all. But they're probably a minority, and if you've always wanted a couple of chickens scratching around or a couple of ducks on the pond then have them. Money isn't the be all and end all, and life is for living. Don't go to your grave regretting the hens you always dreamed of: just get them.

But there are caveats. One is that keeping any sort of livestock, from poultry to bullocks, on any more than a domestic scale involves a lot of regulation, long hours and no holidays. Another is that as live animals, unlike rows of brassica or fruit trees, have minds of their own that might not always chime with yours. If your only experience with livestock has been owning dogs or cats, you may understandably feel a little nervous at the prospect of coercing a reluctant ram, especially if you are small of stature, elderly or physically challenged in any way. In fact even the most hale and strapping of novices will find that moving, shearing, birthing and otherwise handling larger animals such as cattle, sheep, pigs and alpacas is somewhat daunting, and I would strongly suggest volunteering to work on a farm first. This will give you a good idea of what animals are like to work with; and agreeing with the rest of your family whether the end product will justify all the effort will save any tears and misunderstandings along the way. For if you are going to keep livestock for meat, then everyone needs to understand that after five or six months lambs have to be taken for slaughter. By that time, fortunately, they've grown out of the cute little baa-lamb stage and become big, slightly smelly sheep. Poultry also have relatively short lives: birds kept for meat tend to be ready at about five months, and layers can pop their clogs at around two years for hybrids and eight for pure bred birds (although they will have stopped laying long before that).

CPH or farm holding number

If you intend to keep cattle (including buffalo), deer, sheep, goats, pigs or more than 50 fowl you will need a County Parish Holding or farm holding number, a nine-figure code mainly used to identify and trace livestock from its point of origin to whoever you sell it on to. The CPH is also the portal to eligibility for subsidies including grants from the Rural Payments Agency and the Forestry Commission and, in England, countryside stewardship payments. You can apply or check if your holding already has a number at **www.gov.uk/guidance/get-a-cph-number-from-the-rural-payments -agency** (in Scotland, find your local Rural Payments and Services office at **www.ruralpayments.org**).

Health, welfare and other regulations

The health and welfare of farm animals and the risk of their transmitting diseases of various kinds to humans are two subjects very dear to Defra's heart, and as a result there are regulations for you to understand and comply with at almost every turn. Fortunately Defra's Animal and Plant Health Agency is there to help with all the advice and information you will need about flock and herd books, medicine books, ear-tagging, movement licences, notification of contagious diseases, slaughter, and all the other requirements you are expected to know about. Contact your field office via **www.gov.uk/government/organisations/animal-and-planthealth-agency** for more information. The field office is also the place to notify of a suspected outbreak of avian flu, foot and mouth, swine vesicular disease or any other contagious illnesses either on your own holding or anyone else's. It also oversees animal movements, which is why you need to complete movement forms before transporting animals when you buy them, sell them, take them to market or the abbattoir, or display them at agricultural shows. Call your field office well in advance and you will be sent a movement form. APHA will also issue you with a flock or herd number that goes on your animals' ear-tags along with your farm holding number. You order, pay for and attach the tags yourself. (The same agency oversees plant health and should be notified of phytopthera, ash dieback and other such diseases that affect nurserymen, Christmas tree growers and many farmers.)

Two links that will teach you all you need to know about farm animal welfare and policies are **www.gov.uk/topic/keeping-farm-animals** and **www.rspca.org.uk/adviceandwelfare.farm**.

Slaughter, deaths and dealing with carcases

APHA also oversees farm animal slaughter. If you are killing for your own table you can do it at home (see the Humane Slaughter Association's website **www.hsa.org** to find out how). If you intend to produce meat for sale to the public, though, you have to use either a licensed abattoir or a licensed mobile slaughterman. See the Food Standard Agency's website **www.food.gov.uk** for a list.

Wherever there is livestock there is also the eventuality of death from old age, illness or trauma. If you have poultry, for instance, you need to be prepared to deal with the results of a visit from a fox, badger, weasel, stoat, mink or even a domestic dog: mental trauma, physical injury and death. Dealing with an injured, terrified chicken or duck is heartbreaking, and you may well have to make a snap choice between trying to save the creature and putting it out of its misery. I had two visits from stray dogs, resulting in 15 chickens being attacked. I had to euthanize six due to extensive injury and or shock, and you have to know how to do it quickly and confidently and be prepared. The HSA has a 50-page PDF on the practical slaughter of poultry on its website that should tell you all you need to know.

Your next consideration is how to dispose of the carcase. You aren't allowed to just bury or burn it on your land: regulations regarding disposal are at **www.gov.uk/guidance/fallen-stock**. They require you to arrange for the animal to be identified, collected and removed by an approved transporter (there's a link to the National Fallen Stock Company on the site) as soon as reasonably practical. If you're lambing, for instance, and have dead ewes and stillborns to dispose of, you may want to wait until you have enough carcases to warrant a collection. Temporary storage in designated bins is allowed as long as you ensure they are animal- and bird-proof and are disinfected after use. You are responsible for all the costs.

Growing feeds and keeping animals

This sector is fast-growing and offers many alternative crops and products for anyone willing to do a little research and take some risks.

Millet, maize and sunflowers are in increasing demand for the bird seed. In 2012 the market was worth £200 million and it's grown since then. It's part of a market for prepared pet foods of all sorts that's worth £1.5 billion – but it's a highly regulated one. Before you start you have to register with your local authority and if your products contains any ingredients of animal origin (e.g. milk, honey, meat, or fish) then you also need approval from APHA and the Veterinary Laboratories Agency. There are strict rules about hygiene during manufacture and about labelling. See EU Regulation (EC) 183/2005 and EU Regulation (EC) 767/2009. More information can be found at **www.pfma.org.uk/uk-pet-food-legislation**.

Poultry

Chickens and other poultry are a good introduction to livestock keeping. You can keep up to 49 birds before you have to register them with APHA, which means it's perfectly practical to learn and experiment on a manageable scale before going into serious production.

Poultry keeping is fairly labour-intensive, though. Almost all birds need housing to protect them from predators and have to be shut in at night and let out in the morning. The houses have to be mucked out regularly too, and the litter is a potent fertiliser. Most poultry have to be fed, and if you don't have a natural duckpond then the water in the ducks' trough needs changing daily. Chickens and ducks will happily undergraze an orchard doing little damage to the trees, keeping the grass short, nibbling new bramble shoots, eating insects and nitrogenating the soil as they go. If you keep fewer than 50 birds you can sell them from the farm or cottage gate or door-to-door or at a local market without having to sign up with APHA, as noted above, and you don't have to mark the eggs with a producer code either. If you have more than 50, though, then to pack and retail eggs yourself or to wholesale them to shops, restaurants, hotels, pubs or other retailers register as an egg producer and packer with APHA online at **www.gov.uk/guidance/eggs-trade-regulations**. It's free and will take all of five minutes, and the site spells out in detail all the rules and regulations concerning hen-keeping.

Labelling regulations are also very easy to comply with: your boxes must bear your name and address, appropriate storage advice and a best-before date which is 28 days from laying, not from packing. You may also wish to describe the eggs as free range, barn eggs or eggs from caged birds, although this isn't compulsory. EU Council Directive 1999/74/EC sets out exactly what each term means, which you can find rendered into intelligible English on Wikipedia. If in doubt, consult your local council's Trading Standards Department that enforces the rules.

Ducks

Ducks need a suitable house and access to water as they need to be able to immerse their heads. They can make a terrible mess of the edges of natural or man-made ponds so instead we used a sunken baby bath surrounded by pebbles. The water never really stayed clean (ducks will happily foul their water), but the pebbles prevented the area turning into a mud-bath and we could remove, empty and replace the baby bath without any major inconvenience. Originally we used an old bathtub but had a horrific incident when one of the ducks couldn't get out and struggled, became exhausted and drowned. So if you're thinking of reusing a full-sized bathtub, install some sort of gangplank to allow the ducks to get out easily.

We kept Aylesbury-Cherry Valley crosses, which were a delight with their antics and happy quacking. They were regular layers and big enough to produce a good meaty carcass quite quickly. In wet winters they could become a bit problematic around young trees as they persisted in 'dibbling' the soil into a muddy morass, which could damage the roots of young trees. To maintain the soil's structure we had to rotate them frequently into fresh pasture. They also needed protection from predators: there's a reason why we use the expression 'a sitting duck' – ducks are a bit silly and ungainly, and slow to escape from a crafty and efficient fox.

If you want to keep ducks and chickens in the same pen or paddock, do ensure you have enough ducks to keep your drake occupied (one drake to 4-8 ducks is a good ratio) or you may find some traumatised and possibly injured chickens! Remember too that the ducks will gobble down all the chickens' food as well as their own.

Geese

Geese are big birds and need a lot of secure pasture to graze. Three geese will make short work of a half-acre paddock and need supplementary corn feeding for a month or so before slaughter. You can't let geese undergraze an orchard because they strip the bark from the trees and eat the leaves from the lower branches. You also get barely one meal from a goose. I can raise two lambs on the same area and supply a family of four with enough meat to eat lamb once a week for a year. Geese do have a well-deserved reputation as guards, though – they can make a lot of noise when someone approaches, and they bite. A goose bite can be extremely sore and, because the birds have a serrated beak, may well draw blood. We were glad to say goodbye to them!

Other poultry

Looking at other feathered creatures, you may wish to consider turkeys or quail. There is a small window of opportunity at Christmas for turkey sales, which may tempt someone who can supply a small local market with corn-fed free-range premium birds. The risk of blackhead or histomoniasis, which can affect all poultry but is particularly severe in turkeys, will be greatly reduced by keeping them apart from other poultry and or barn-rearing them.

Quail will supply both the small eggs so beloved of high-class restaurants and birds ready for the table. Quail are not a regular item in UK supermarkets, but if you have access to restaurants or if you produce for a bespoke clientele, then they may be a project worth considering. With carefully-controlled indoor rearing you can produce birds and eggs almost year-round, and a female bird can produce around 180 eggs. So from hatching to laying takes around six weeks, and they're ready to eat at nine weeks. They don't need a huge amount of space, but it must be rat-proof, well ventilated and heated in winter.

Guinea fowl present a particular problem in that they don't like roosting and are quite difficult to round up. They prefer to roost in trees and are therefore particularly vulnerable to foxes.

Avian flu

The increasing threat of avian flu, especially in coastal areas where migrating birds tend to congregate, means you have to provide your flock with enclosed and secure housing and runs in case a Prevention Zone is declared. This last occurred in winter 2016 and continued all the way into spring 2017. Enforced housing not only increases your feed, heating and lighting costs, it can also affect the market price of your eggs because if the birds are housed for any length of time, the eggs and carcases can no longer be sold as free range. Luckily it's still rare, but if you have a sudden rise in bird mortality and suspect avian flu contact both your vet and APHA field office immediately: it's a notifiable disease.

Bees

Bees produce so much value and perform such useful services that it's a wonder more people don't keep them. They thrive in warm, sheltered areas with abundant and varied vegetation. Most fruit growers and arable farmers are happy to site some colonies on their land as the introduction of pollinators only increases their crops. If you decide to house some – either your own or someone else's – in your orchard, your apple crop will increase by as much as a third. Fencing off the beehives will afford them some protection from undergrazing poultry and any larger livestock. They require almost no work in winter, and checking weekly in spring and autumn to ensure against swarming and to provide new supers for the bees to store honey in only takes around 20 minutes per hive. The honey is usually harvested in August before applying a varroa treatment to each hive.

The varroa mite is now found all over the UK and a bad infestation can severely affect a colony, but treatment is simple and should be carried out as a matter of course by all beekeepers. A new threat to British honeybees in the UK is the arrival in 2016 of Asian hornets (*Vespa velutina*), voracious predators of the native honeybee and other beneficial insects. They have a dark brown body and head with a distinctive orange/yellow face.

There is a great deal of information on beekeeping on the internet, and the ideal site to visit before plunging in is the British Beekeepers Association **www.bbka.org.uk**. There are also many plans available on the internet if you are interested in building your own traditional or top bar hive. A nice book with good illustrations suitable for new or experienced beekeepers is *The Complete Step-by-Step Book of Beekeeping* by David Cramp. The late Dave Cushman developed a wonderful website devoted to bees that is still accessible and well worth delving into: **www.dave-cushman.net**. For a very watchable foretaste of what to expect, have a look at this Beekeeping for Beginners DVD extract **www.youtube.com/watch?v=-fMlJoeEQcA**.

Sheep

Raising lambs as a high-value project worked for us – we realised three times what it cost to produce and butcher them, and we never needed to cut the grass where they had been. They arrived in the first week of March, were bottle-fed for around a month then weaned on to grass; and they were outside by May. They went off to the abattoir at the end of October. No shearing, no winter feeding. We kept two lambs on half an acre, one for our own consumption and one to sell. If we had had more land we would have developed it as it a guaranteed easy income.

A stocking density of 6-10 sheep per acre (all year) is feasible depending on the quality of pasture you can provide but keeping sheep all year is more costly and labour intensive. The year begins with lambing in early spring; lambing is normally managed indoors and the lambs are turned outside to fresh pasture as soon as they are thriving. They are not shorn in their first year, but older hoggets or mature sheep need their fleeces removed when the weather turns warmer; usually in May. This is a good time for a general health check of the flock. As autumn approaches, ewes are selected for breeding and a ram is put in with them with a coloured crayon or dye on his chest to indicate which ewes he has served. Traditionally the ram was put in with the ewes on Bonfire night so that lambing wouldn't start until April when the weather was kinder; modern farmers tend to put the ram in at least a month earlier to have earlier lambs for market. Breeding ewes usually produce twins, which can be kept and fattened for four–six months before slaughtering. Ewes can produce lambs from their second year until around the age of six or seven before productivity dips.

Different breeds have different characteristics. The Hebridean is small, black-fleeced, usually slaughtered at six months but also good for mutton. Cheviots are larger with white fleeces and are more lively and active. Herdwick sheep are very hardy. Suffolks are big and good for meat. They have white fleeces and chocolate faces and legs. Rylands are almost like teddy bears: woolly faces and legs, medium sized and very docile. Of course you can also get commercial crosses such as Beltex, Texel, mules etc. The more native and close to the wild the sheep you choose, the less docile and more adventurous they seem to be.

Goats

Goats are an option for both meat and dairy production. They can be the Houdinis of the animal world, though, so excellent fencing is required; and the uncastrated males have a pungent, lingering odour. You will need shelter for them as their coats are not waterproof and prolonged exposure to poor weather will make them ill; you'll also need a small milking parlour if you're going to keep dairy goats. They will destroy an orchard but they do very well on rough, stony ground. Goats are browsers rather than grazers so they need more space than sheep, say 6-8 animals per acre on reasonable pasture. They will improve the pasture by eating weeds cattle will leave, so could follow cattle.

There are a number of breeds available in the UK suitable for different purposes and locations. Toggenburgs are good dairy goats and can produce milk for two to three years after kidding. Making the cheese yourself will increase your profitability by a good margin. Perhaps using a good meat sire such as a Boer would produce kids for meat and thus supply two markets as goat meat is gaining in popularity in the UK with great demand from Asian and Caribbean buyers, especially just before religious festivals. You can find more at **www.britishgoatsociety.com**.

Pigs

Pigs can be an ideal animal for the smallholder. They can clear scrubby, overgrown areas and manure it as they go, eat vegetable waste from the smallholding and orchard (in addition to proper pig nuts) and will provide you with lovely meat. Be wary of stories about certain breeds of pigs being safe to release into an orchard, though. All pigs dig and will destroy an orchard if kept there for longer than it takes to eat the windfalls. Electric fencing at 6" and 12" (checked daily) and dry movable housing are important. They are natural woodland beasts, so fencing off part of a wood is ideal, but they will quickly transform normal pasture into a scene from World War I. They're social animals, so you need to keep at least two, and unless you have a very large market for your meat a couple of weaners of the same sex at a time will probably suffice. Whether you choose gilts or boars is a matter for personal preference and stories of boar taint seem to be a myth, according to all the pig keepers I've spoken to. Oh, and just a heads up for all you people considering micro-pigs – there is no such thing! All pigs are small as piglets, but they all grow into large pigs.

You could stock as many as six weaners an acre for a period of around 5-6 weeks with additional feeding as long as you are prepared for total clearance of the land, which will need to be left to recover

Case study:
Alex and Andy Lee, Waterlooville, Hampshire

Alex and Andy Lee started their smallholding on 9½ acres in Finchdean near Waterlooville in 2002. Both had retired and were seeking a sustainable lifestyle not too ruthlessly commercial. Soil Association members, they are committed to biodiversity and avoid the use of artificial fertilisers, herbicides and pesticides – practices that benefit the quality of the meat as well as wildlife and the landscape. The smallholding is on sloping ground with some natural shade and is divided into five fields of pasture and subdivided into 10 plots. It's prone to flooding thanks to the Lavant, a winterbourne that only fills seasonally but is still perfectly capable of bursting its banks, and groundwater that can bubble up from the soil and cause floods after heavy rain.

Apart from a few chickens, the Lees' livestock comprises 41 Badge-Faced Welsh Mountain or Torddhu sheep, including a breeding ram. The Torddhu is a hardy upland sheep known for its sweet and tender meat. The fleeces make only a slight profit over the cost of shearing and are sold to the Wool Marketing Board for around £1 a kilo, with each sheep yielding 2-6kg. Occasionally the skins have been made into sheepskin rugs, but it's an increasingly difficult procedure because there are so few working tanneries left. Expect to pay around £25 per skin to have it tanned (see **www.devoniaproducts.co.uk**.)

They manage the smallholding and animals themselves but subcontract shearing and fencing and buy in the hay they need for winter feed. The animals are slaughtered and butchered locally at just over £20 per animal. Their meat is only sold locally. The Lees are members of the local Small Shepherds Club **www.smallshepherdsclub.org.uk,** which promotes good husbandry of smaller flocks and offers training to small flock owners.

significantly. You could try a three-year rotation, planting a third of your land with roots such as turnip and a third with legumes or maize and using the final third as pig pasture. A survey by the Green Pig Project in conjunction with Defra has shown that native legumes provide adequate protein and nutritional value when used as a feed additive and reduce reliance on expensive and unethical soya mixes.

Pigs can be ready for slaughter as early as four months depending on feeding and intended use. It used to be that pigs were more economical to keep than lambs; sadly due to rising feed costs this is no longer the case unless you bulk out processed pig feed with home-grown feed crops and other supplements. But have a care: feeding kitchen or catering scraps to pigs is now illegal. This is to prevent the introduction and spread of notifiable diseases such as swine fever and foot and mouth disease. See **www.gov.uk/government/news/apha-warns-not-to-feed-kitchen-scraps-to-farm-animals-because-of-disease-risk**. There's more information on feeding pigs at **www.britishpigs.org.uk/alternative_feeds_for_pigs.pdf**.

Cattle

Even a small smallholding can support some breeds of cattle. Dexter's, for example, are ideal smallholding cattle, and you can stock one adult per acre. Killing at 20–24 months will produce 150-220kg of meat depending on the animal and the butcher. As with lamb and pork, there is always a good market for home-produced beef, and some processing of the cheaper, less popular cuts will increase sales. It has been claimed that miniature cattle consume 40 per cent less food than standard cattle but produce 60 per cent by weight of prime cuts. Naturally, this needs to be evaluated, but it makes for good reading: **www.pocketfarm.co.uk/mini-moos-the-world-most-popular-beef-cattle-repackaged-for-smallholders/**.

A good way to start would be to get one in-calf cow with a youngster at foot. This way, you have company for the cattle and a supply of meat to grow on. Dexter's are thrifty, easy to tame, good mothers and long-lived, so with good management you could get both milk and beef for many years. They will need hay and any roots you can supply in the winter: allow half a small bale to feed one beast daily.

Many owners bring the cattle in for the winter to prevent poaching of the ground in wet weather and to keep an eye on calving. Naturally this will increase feed and bedding costs, and extra labour will also be necessary to feed the animals and clean out and re-bed their housing.

An additional point to consider is the incidence of TB in the UK, and there are rules and costs involved in TB testing and movement. These vary from region to region, so contact APHA and get some advice if you are considering owning cattle.

Alpacas

There is a considerable debate about alpacas in the UK farming and rural scene. It appears that you either love them or hate them. Personally, I don't really see the point of alpacas: there is no market for their meat and getting a crop of fleece isn't easy. The British Alpaca Society says on its website, **www.bas-uk.com**, that "a vibrant marketplace for alpaca fibre is emerging", but they are an expensive purchase and need to be kept as a herd. The stocking rate is 5–6 per good quality acre. They require shearing to produce 3–5kg of fibre once a year, usually in July, as well as regular foot trimming. They can be out-wintered, but benefit from winter shelter.

Shearing an alpaca normally requires two or three people. Two people lift the beast and lay it on one side (unlike a sheep, which is sat on its rump). The legs are then tethered to prevent the animal from moving and injuring itself or others. The handler holds the head of the alpaca while the shearer shears the body down one side, then the animal is rolled and turned to allow the other side to be sheared. This takes roughly six minutes per alpaca.

Small herds of alpaca are sometimes kept alongside sheep and poultry primarily to deter foxes rather than for the value of their wool (although it really is valuable as knitting yarn, either pure or blended). In their native South America fox-type predators are known to take cria (baby alpacas), and in the wild adult alpacas will chase foxes and trampled them to death if they catch them. Here in Britain they are semi-domesticated and not so fierce, but foxes still stay away.

Hedging and fencing

Fences and hedges that will keep your stock in and unwanted visitors, be it foxes, deer or rabbits, out are expensive capital items that have to be constantly checked and maintained and regularly replaced. Even tanalised fenceposts will only last 7-8 years. Nevertheless boundary protection is important and should never be neglected since the consequences can be dire.

Hedges are certainly more appealing visually, and harbour a wealth of insects to feed wild birds such as sparrows, but they do need to be thick and spiny right from the ground up. If a hedge becomes gappy at the bottom it can be cut and relaid to make it stockproof. The new growth will shoot vertically from stems that are almost cut through horizontally and then laid almost flat. You might be advised to entrust this highly-skilled task to a professional, but there are detailed instructions and a video at **www.woodlands.co.uk**. A well-laid boundary hedge will only need a light trim of the sides and top for the first ten years or so before a substantial overhaul is required.

A dense hedge is an effective windbreak, sheltering livestock from the icy blast and helping prevent dry soil from blowing away in hot spells. It also provides a whole ecosystem for many useful plant varieties: sloes for gin and vodka; hazels for nuts, pea-sticks and walking sticks; damsons and bullace for wine, pies and liqueurs; and elder for both blossom and berries, which make fine wines and a lovely light elderflower cordial.

Food and Drink

05

Case Studies

Producing food or drink from your smallholding, allotment or garden is perhaps the most obvious way of deriving an income from it. And although everyone's circumstances are unique, the diversity of possible projects is so great that there is bound to be something to suit. If you have hardly any land, for instance, you can still grow enough fruit and vegetables to make jellies, jams, juices, chutneys, pickles and the like; and you can make your processing equipment (ordinary domestic kitchen appliances aren't really up to this kind of use) work harder for its living by foraging hedgerows, moors and even beaches for wild ingredients. Anyone with even a small orchard can produce culinary and dessert apples and pears, juice, cider, perry and vinegar for sale: I have devoted a whole chapter to orchards for a very good reason – they make money! A few acres will allow you to keep goats or sheep for milk and cheese. Five acres or more is room enough for a few smaller-breed cattle.

Whatever project you decide suits your own situation best, though, make sure to do your sums as carefully as if you were writing a full-blown business plan; and you'd be well-advised to major on one or two high-value strands to maximise your income and to rationalise the cost and effort involved in production, processing and selling.

Eggs

I'll start with egg production because it's an enterprise in which I have fairly extensive experience, and because at entry level it's one of the easiest ways to make a bit of pocket-money from your land. You can sell eggs at the gate without any regulation: all you need is a sign with the price on it. But although it may be comparatively easy, it's never going to make you a millionaire. You can sell a box of six eggs at around £1.50, but that has to cover the cost of the hens, their housing, their feed, boxes and labels, and worming and vet's bills before you see any of it. If you have fewer than 100 hens you'll make just enough to cover your costs, which is fine if the hens are a hobby. But to make any money out of laying birds you have to think of them as a crop that needs replacing every 18 months or so, so there's a recurring capital cost to factor in as well. Duck eggs will fetch a similar price, but the laying season is shorter and therefore your income will be lower unless you also hatch and raise some of them for meat.

These sums might prompt you to ask yourself whether the return is going to be worth the effort. I was an egg producer and packer for two years before realising it was too much work for the reward. I would have needed larger henhouses, a higher stocking density and at least 500 birds to make even a small wage. But the profit from selling eggs is not going to provide you with a living unless you have thousands; and even at this level the input on your part – such as moving their houses regularly to deter rodents and prevent soil erosion – is beginning to mount up alarmingly. By the time you reach a genuinely profitable level of egg production your capital investment, not just in housing but in ancillaries such as automated packaging plant, packing shed(s) and feed silos, and your additional running costs including labour, feed, bedding and utilities takes you beyond the scale at which you can really be described as a smallholder. However, if you believe that large-scale egg production is a viable proposition – and as the EU allows a maximum of 1,000 hens per acre it may very well suit your circumstances – you will also have to register as a food producer with the district council's Environmental Health Department (see below). Large poultry houses with a packing room and feed silos also need planning permission, so have a chat with your local planning officer before making any commitments.

Between the two extremes of selling a few eggs as a sideline and going into large-scale production there is the option of keeping pure-breed chickens, which allows you to exploit the highly profitable internet hatching-egg business. Raising the rarer breeds means you can command higher prices for the eggs without increasing your costs, so concentrate on a couple of breeds you like and raise the best birds you can. Our third of an acre paddock supported 40 birds, although we could have managed more. We kept Orpingtons as they laid well, produced a good meaty carcase and were easy to manage. We kept separate breeding groups of Blue, Black, Buff and Lavender Orpingtons. The eggs were very popular, and living in Cornwall meant that the birds were laying fertile eggs earlier than in other parts of the UK and that I could get a jump on the market, which also meant higher prices. Where I could sell a box of six eggs for £1.50 for eating, I got £20 as hatching eggs, and my hatching egg season started in February and finished at the end of June. Half a dozen chickens and a cockerel per group gave me up to six eggs daily over 150 days, which paid for the housing, feed, bills, polystyrene postage boxes and replacement hens, provided my family with fresh eggs and made me a bit of profit too.

Duck eggs have a ready market as eating eggs, but if you keep a pure breed and at least one fertile drake you can also offer them as hatching eggs. With an incubator and a spare secure house can also hatch replacement birds and some for meat. From hatch to dispatch for meat is only 16 weeks and there is always demand for a nice young duck! They lay seasonally, and you can expect eggs daily from February to June.

The more hens you have, the more manure you have. At a rough estimate 50 hens will produce about two tonnes of manure per acre of pasture per year, which is why rotating pasture is important. And alongside all that nitrogen, potassium and phosphorus will be a sizeable worm burden and possible insect infestations which, if you are keeping chickens for eggs or meat, you'll have to monitor very carefully. But litter from the henhouse – bedding and manure – doesn't have to be composted or otherwise treated to provide a good surface fertiliser. An average tonne of poultry litter contains around 25kg each of nitrogen and phosphate and 20kg of potash as well as trace amounts of all the other essential elements for plant growth. If dug in it is also a source of organic matter for the soil. To avoid pollution of surface waters, though, do not apply poultry litter near ponds, streams or rivers or on steep slopes where it will wash away as soon as it rains.

Cheese

Cheesemaking is a project often taken up by ex-dairy farmers. They already own a lot of the equipment they need, they're used to the unsocial hours (especially the early starts!) and they can make more profit from artisan cheese than from bulk milk. Some stick to cows, but many either add a few sheep and or goats or go over to them entirely. They're easier to manage and can be stocked at higher density, and surplus offspring can be reared for meat. In capital terms it can be an expensive business: you'll need all the housing and equipment associated with stockrearing (see below) and a dairy room, milking parlour, milk tanks, cheese vat, pasteurising equipment, storage facilities and packaging equipment. DairyCo has an online guide that prospective cheesemakers can download for free. The On Farm Small Scale Cheese Making Guide was published in 2009 so is out of date as far as prices are concerned, but the technical information is still current. Visit **www.dairy.ahdb.org.uk**. At time of writing it would cost about £10,000 to equip a small goat or sheep dairy for about 10 animals, including parlour and milking equipment, if you bought second-hand. Pasteurisation equipment and carton sealing equipment could cost a further £8,000 second-hand.

Many artisans today make cheese without owning any livestock at all and instead buy their raw milk from a supplier, preferably a small specialist one. This makes the raw material more expensive but cuts out the need for a milking parlour or even any land, and also reduces the running costs in terms of stock management, feed and labour to zero. To explore this option visit **ribblesdalecheese.wordpress.com**. Ribblesdale is also one of many small farms offering training courses. See also **www.westhighlanddairy.co.uk**. Further searches will reveal many others.

Next you need to decide what kind of cheese to produce – soft, hard, blue, crumbly, mild, tangy, cream, cottage, nutty, smoked: there are as many options as there are makers. Cash flow will form an important part of your decision: soft cheeses don't need to mature, so you get a quicker return on your capital; hard cheeses customarily mature for at least nine months, so although they usually command a higher price you do need a bigger float. Thorough market research is probably even more important in helping you decide, though. In particular, gain a thoroughly knowledge of the retail outlets in your area. What types of cheese do they stock? What do they charge?

Who makes it and who buys it? One way to identify and fill a gap in the market is to team up with a good specialist retailer who will suggest what you should make and why, and will also do most of the marketing and selling for you. But do remember: artisan cheese is serious stuff. It's expensive and it needs to look, feel and taste expensive. Try to develop a cheese with a genuine local connection and a unique appearance or flavour. A novelty cheese may get people smiling or buying it for a joke, but you won't get much repeat business. The retailers you are out to impress – delicatessens, upscale farm shops, serious publicans, hoteliers and restaurateurs – as well as the foodies who flock to farmers' markets love the 'local' tag, but it has to be backed up by substance: style accuracy, balance, depth of flavour, correct texture and overall quality.

Other dairy products

When the enzyme rennet is added to cow's milk, the liquid separates into about 85 per cent curds and 15 per cent whey, rich in lactose and protein, which commercial creameries sell in huge quantities to manufacturers of milk formula for babies and, more recently, protein powder for athletes and bodybuilders. Given the small quantities you're likely to produce you may be tempted simply to spray it on your pasture as a soil conditioner or use it to supplement your animals' feed. But in sufficient quantities it has many uses and therefore a monetary value. If you're buying in raw milk, for instance, you might return the whey to your supplier for these self-same purposes against a discount on the price of your next delivery. It's very low in fat and can be used as the basis for whey cheeses, of which the best-known is ricotta and the weirdest is surely brunost. It can be used instead of water in all kinds of dough – for bread, when its mild acidity stimulates the yeast, and for cake, biscuits and pastry, when its slight sweetness enriches and deepens the flavour. It can be pasteurised and possibly flavoured as a genuine health drink, although the market outside Iceland and Switzerland might be a little niche. And it can be fermented too, with a special yeast called *Kluyveromyces marxianus* (lactose is immune to beer and wine yeast) to make a sour beer similar to Central Asian kumiss (although kumiss is made of whole milk), which can then be distilled to make arak. All of these are potential earners, so don't just throw your whey away!

Whey and its products are perhaps a little bit out of the mainstream, but yoghurt and ice-cream certainly aren't; and the advantage of yoghurt and ice-cream over cheese is the same as soft cheese over hard: a much quicker return.

Ice cream can be particularly important for the small-scale dairy farmer. It's a huge growth industry that is apparently recession-proof, and one that you can make a good living from if you have a unique selling point and good marketing. As a ballpark figure and using the traditional method, every litre of ice cream mix costs around £1.70 to produce and sells at around £18 net. Not bad!

Your first step is to decide on a product: organic natural ice cream, full fat premium ice cream or frozen yoghurt. Then you need to consider the available sales channels – your own shop or cafe, a strategically located kiosk or third-party tearooms, farm shops, delicatessens, cafes, pubs, restaurants? What equipment will you need at point of sale – display freezers, a striking and characterful old-fashioned trike or handcart or a straightforward ice cream van? Finally, price your product to be competitive without underselling yourself: a premium price denotes a premium product.

The obstacle to getting into the ice-cream business is the specialised equipment it requires. Firstly all the raw ingredients need to be mixed, cooked, blended to emulsify and then pasteurised (not compulsory but very, very highly recommended), which can all be carried out using everyday catering equipment. The mixture then has to be chilled down rapidly, certainly within 90 minutes, to 4–7°C. Normally this is when you split the batch and add your chosen flavourings. Finally the mixture should be frozen to -6°C while being whipped or churned. An added complication is that freezing doesn't kill toxic bacteria, so everything has to be mega-clean.

Basic dairy ice cream is the cheapest to make, but that's not saying much! A single machine will pasteurise, cool and store it before it is flavoured and frozen in a batch freezer. A 3-in-1 machine with a capacity of up to 30kg/hour will cost around £25,000 new; a new batch freezer can cost £12,600. Gelato display cabinets create good visual presentation: a new one holding 12 pans can cost £8,000. Extra pans can be stored in a simple chest or upright freezer. Get details of equipment and demonstration days at **www.rsshereford.co.uk**.

Yoghurt is made by fermenting milk and adding colourings and flavours. Like cheese, the milk is coagulated into curds but with a lactobacillus culture rather than rennet. The bacilli digest the milk sugars and excrete lactic acid, which curdles the milk. The milk is first heated to 82°C to kill off any unwanted microorganisms, then cooled to 43°C when the lactobacillus culture is added. Full-cream cow's or ewe's milk produces thick yoghurt while semi-skimmed produces a thinner one. Once it has cooled and thickened it can be sold as plain yoghurt or can have honey or fruit added. The equipment required is similar to that used in cream or cheese making, and the suppliers are often the same. I've added a link here for a yoghurt maker, but have a look at the other related items the company supplies: **www.gnltd.co.uk/goat-nutrition/smallholder-equipment/elecrem-y140-yogurt-maker.html**.

With equipment for commercial producers starting at around £3,000 for a 140-pot batch electric yoghurt maker, this could be a good start-up business, especially if you can produce your own raw ingredients. Although the market for yoghurt has been stable for the last five years, consumers are switching from mass-produced basic yoghurt to naturally-sweetened, high-welfare, artisan and organic brands. The market is also becoming more diverse with buttermilk, kefir, and other fermented dairy produce now widely available.

Jams, preserves and chutneys

A favourite diversification project that keeps coming up on courses I have run or at food fairs and markets I have attended is that of jams and chutneys. Now, I like jam as much as the next person, but I'm going to look at this as a business proposition.

First, you need to produce a product that is going to jump out as very special to the customer. This may be because you have produced something very rare or the packaging is very luxurious; whatever it is it has to be different enough from all the other jams or chutneys or sauces on the same shelf.

Second, you need to be serious about your overall costs. They include growing inputs and picking time or price of raw materials if they're bought in; preparation time; electricity/gas (tip: use a microwave whenever possible!); packaging and labelling; and sales and marketing including trade samples, courier costs, stall fees etc. Then you need to work out a price you think a customer will realistically pay, either close to comparable products or outrageously more expensive. If you end up with a gross profit of 50p a jar, you need to sell 30,000 jars a year to make a wage of £15,000. That means selling 125 jars at farmers' markets and food fairs five days a week for 48 weeks a year. Now, this may be a good little earner for the occasional food fair or Christmas market to bring in an additional income stream, especially if you grow the produce yourself; but if you are thinking of it as a possible business, there are less time-consuming and more lucrative possibilities.

Honey and beeswax

Beekeeping is one of those activities like poultry keeping where you can start small, covering your costs while you gain in confidence and skill, and gradually expand into meaningful profitability without ever having to fund a large capital outlay.

The best way to start is to visit the British Beekeepers' Association website **www.bbka.org.uk** where you will find a contact for your local beekeepers' club or group. Joining plugs you instantly into a network of experienced and normally very helpful enthusiasts who can find you second-hand starter gear such as hives, a beesuit, a smoker and a few tools and spares for not an awful lot of money. As for the bees themselves, a good colony with a young laying queen may well set you back £180, or a small starter colony or 'nuc' comprising five frames of bees, brood and a young queen upwards of £100. Club members might let you have stock cheap, and the bees you buy from them will be adapted to local conditions.

You don't even need much land to set up as a hobby beekeeper. A single colony takes up less than two foot square, and if there is ample and diverse forage available within a two or three-mile radius you can house several colonies in a fairly small garden. Friends and neighbours might well host pollinators in their own gardens, trading the certainty of increased yields of fruit, vegetables and flowers against the vanishingly low risk of the occasional sting (honey bees are very docile creatures). Fruit and arable farmers also welcome visiting hives, either permanently or in spring when many of them will gladly pay for pollination services. You might find yourself in competition with other local beekeepers for the best sites; on the other hand you might find them very co-operative in introducing you to potential customers. And if you find yourself having to transport hives to and from temporary sites, they'll be fine on the back of a pick-up or even in the boot of your car provided you follow these golden rules: fit entrance reducers; plug all holes, even ventilation holes; don't scrimp on the duct tape – use as much as you possibly can to cover every exit, hole, and seam of the hive; and if you liberate the bees as soon as you arrive at your destination and they'll come to no harm.

Most hobby and novice beekeepers have a couple of colonies in case one fails. A medium-sized honey operation may comprise 20–30 colonies, most of them kept at different sites. An efficient part-time business could operate up to 100 or so colonies sited reasonable distances apart. In a really good year, a healthy hive could produce 60lbs of honey; in a poor year you might get no return at all. Look for an average of 33lbs. The going rate for local honey at time of writing is around £6 per pound of runny, creamed or set honey, with much higher prices for cut-comb and heather honey.

There is some debate over whether honey should be pasteurised before sale: one side says that the small risk of botulism from raw honey makes pasteurisation a safe bet; the other side says that pasteurisation not only kills bad bugs but good ones as well, and destroys much of the flavour into the bargain. The most obvious thing to do is simply to fill the honey into jars and sell it, either in its natural state, which is clear and runny, or as the 'creamed' or 'set' honey that is more familiar to the average consumer. To set or cream natural honey takes a bit of work, though. Most honey will granulate naturally as its sucrose content crystallises: to help the process along, store a 1lb jar at 12–15C. When it has set into coarse granules, beat it until it's smooth. Mix it into another 4lbs of runny honey and repeat the process. Now mix the smooth honey into a bucket containing 40lbs of runny honey and, again, beat it smooth. You will almost certainly require mechanical assistance to give a meaningful beating to 45lbs of sticky gloop: a power-drill fitted with a grout mixer and run at its slowest speed should do the trick. The large producer will require rather more sophisticated equipment! Now fill your mixture into jars and store them at 14C/58F for up to a week, when they'll be ready for sale.

The UK currently produces only around 14 per cent of the honey it needs, so there is ample potential for the independent beekeeper to enter the market. Local honey commands a premium over commercially-produced competitors, although finding retail space may be difficult in districts where competition is strong. Beeswax is another high-value product prized by artisan makers of cosmetics, candles and wood-polish: a wholesale price of £7 a pound for unrefined block wax at time of writing is far from unreasonable and of course if you or anyone in your household cares to process it yourself the sky is the limit.

Once you have gained enough experience, two further profit opportunities present themselves: producing nucs or starter colonies in spring to sell to newcomers or to expand existing colonies, and training the newcomers themselves.

Mead, country wines, and liqueurs

Honey is also the precursor to a very traditional and possibly ancient alcoholic drink: mead. Because it's made of honey mead is commonly thought of as being very sweet but of course, that's nonsense. The sweetness of the finished product depends entirely on how much of its sugar has been digested during fermentation: it can indeed be cloyingly syrupy, if that's what the meadmaker wants; on the other hand it can equally well be as dry and delicate as a fino sherry.

Case study
Polmarkyn Dairy, Katie Wood and Glyn Thomas, Brook Barn Farm, Liskeard, Cornwall
www.polmarkyndairy.co.uk

Katie and Glyn Thomas bought their 18-acre farm only in early 2016, so their business is a fairly new venture. Glyn is a mechanic, but Katie has some experience as a dairymaid at a farm in Gloucestershire.

Brook Barn Farm is actually a small cottage with some outbuildings surrounded by typical small Cornish paddocks of medium to poor grazing in a hilly area prone to flooding, which taken together can all prove challenging. That's on top of a working day that starts at 4am with milking and can last through the night in kidding season.

"If you have a dream, go for it!" says Katie. "We make enough to cover bills, but we are here all the time and have no social life, which suits us."

Katie and Glyn run a small herd of around 50 female pedigree goats and have turned the old farm buildings into a dairy and winter housing (goats don't like the rain!). The herd is a mixture of British Alpine, British Toggenburg, Golden Guernsey and British Saanen goats.

The farm's income is derived from sales of fresh milk, yoghurt and white, grey and blue goats' cheeses, although eventually Katie hopes to sell meat from the goats as well. All the milk is raw and unpasteurised, and it took some effort to persuade the district council's environmental health department that the products were safe. Fortunately the Specialist Cheesemakers' Association and Cornwall County Council had formalised a code of practice only three years previously that established guidelines for the safe handling of unpasteurised milk: if you're thinking of following the same path, here they are in full: **www.specialistcheesemakers.co.uk/assured-guide.aspx**.

Polmarkyn won a gold medal at the 2017 Cornish Cheese and Dairy Awards for its milk, which it now supplies to a London restaurant. It also supplies milk and cheese to Jamie Oliver's Fifteen restaurant in Cornwall. The dairy now has its own licence to sell all their home-produced products direct to the public and have now opened an online shop. All deliveries are via courier and come in double boxes to keep products cool. You can even collect direct from the farm during the week, but ensure you call ahead.

Producing alcoholic drinks such as mead, country wines and liqueurs (cider is something of a special case) is a not unusual part of a smallholder's business. If you can make a good product and your marketing appeals to a select audience (the Queen of Denmark regularly orders mead from a friend of mine) then this may well be a worthwhile string to your beekeeping bow. It's yet another of those areas where you can start small and cover your costs as you go until, once you're confident you know what you're doing, you can expand to the point where the business is genuinely profitable. When making a mini-business plan to work out your costs and likely receipts, you'll find that the raw materials are fairly cheap, even if you don't necessarily grow them all yourself; the starter kit is a selection of buckets and troughs, along with a crusher and press for juicing soft fruits both of which you can get second-hand or quite cheaply through a company such as Vigo Ltd **www.vigoltd.com**; and bottling and labelling can be managed by hand, mind-numbing though it undoubtedly is. A disadvantage is that the return isn't quick: a well-made mead or fruit wine can take up to a year to mature. Another advantage, though, is that your enterprise will be almost unopposed by large-scale commercial manufacturers: there is no longer a single nationally-distributed genuinely nationally-distributed brand of country wines except those that are, like British fortified wines and most ginger wines, based on imported grape concentrate rehydrated, fermented and flavoured. They have negligible marketing budgets and no pretensions to premium status (or pricing), all of which means that you can enter the market on your own terms.

The big drawback, which is quite big enough to deter many people, is that you are entering the realm of Her Majesty's Revenue and Customs, a place where time and money somehow learn how to disappear. It's not quite as difficult as you think, though – or at least not at first. To produce any kind of alcohol for sale you need an excise licence, which you can apply for online at **www.gov.uk/guidance/wine-duty**. It's free, and the only tricky bit so far is supplying a site plan with the putative positions of all your various bits and pieces of equipment – crusher, press, fermenting vessels and conditioning vessels – clearly marked. After that, though, you get down to reading in full Excise Notice 163 setting out in detail the many and varied record-keeping and reporting requirements at every stage of the process, and your head begins to spin. That's when you ask whether all the kerfuffle is going to be worth it; and that's when you go back to the profits forecast you made earlier. If the figures still look tempting then reassure yourself by reflecting that hundreds of others no cleverer than you learn and live by all these procedures without apparent difficulty, and if they can so can you.

Mead and fruit wines are taxed as 'made wine', a category that embraces any alcoholic drink that isn't beer, cider (or perry), grape wine, or distilled spirits. At time of writing the duty bands are: 1.2-4 % ABV – £88.93 per hectolitre; 4-5.5% – £122.30. 5.5-15% – £288.65; 15-22% - £384.22. If the drink is sparkling then the duty bands and current rates are: 5.5-8.5% – £279.45; 8.5-22% – £369.72. One very useful tip here, though: the fermentable material in old country drinks such as ginger 'beer' and nettle 'beer' is usually either sugar and or honey; they are therefore classed and taxed as made wine. A nettle 'beer' maker in Dorset recently discovered this to her cost: she owed so much in unpaid duty that it put her out of business. If the fermentable base you use is malt extract, though, the product is classed and taxed as beer.

Liqueurs are a different class of drink altogether. Adding value to any raw product to enhance both its profitability and saleability is a fundamental in the smallholder's business ethos. A punnet of raspberries won't make much profit, for example; but a jar of raspberry jam will produce more and a bottle of spirit-based raspberry liqueur more still. Branching out into this style of product requires a new mini-business plan, for while the production itself is both cheap and easy, the cost of ingredients and the compliance input are rather greater.

If you make a liqueur by compounding or maceration (i.e. by buying ready-made ethanol and adding fruit or other flavourings to it) you have to get a licence from HMRC as a compounder simply by completing form L5, which you will find at **www.gov.uk/guidance/spirits-duty**. You also have to 'make entry' (in plain speech, make a detailed list) of the premises and plant you intend to use. To do this, complete either form EX103 for sole traders or form EX103A for registered companies. HMRC has no discretion to refuse these applications, provided they are properly made out.

If the finished product's ABV is between 15–22% you will still in theory pay duty at the same rate as on made wine. Actually what happens is that you buy in pure ethanol – suppliers include Alcohols Ltd of Langley Green, Birmingham, and Haymankimia of Witham, Essex – paying the full spirits duty of £28.74 a litre at time of writing. If you simply liquored it down to, say, 20% ABV that would be £5.75 a litre, £4.31 a bottle or £2.87 for the increasingly popular 50cl. This compares badly with the made wine equivalents of £3.84, £2.88 and £1.92. If you are already an excise warehouse (and the chances are that you're not) you can buy the spirit duty-free ('in duty suspension') and only pay the made-wine rate once the liqueur is ready to sell. But as you're not an excise warehouse you have to pay the full duty on the spirit and then use the process known as drawback to reclaim the difference. Actually the best person to talk you through the process is your ethanol supplier. They do this all the time and know the ropes backwards. Make sure your production records are spot on, though – messing with HMRC is not for the faint-hearted! Neither of the main suppliers publish price-lists today, but to give you a very rough idea to help you plan, in 2015 Haymankimia charged £350 plus duty and VAT for a 25l can, with the price dropping very steeply on larger orders. If you're serious about the idea, then get an up-to-date price on application and produce a really accurate plan. Given the costs and the price that premium artisan liqueurs can command you can see that there's a healthy margin to be made, especially in the run-up to Christmas when the 50cl size makes an ideal gift.

Before you dive in, though, do some product testing in your own kitchen. Vodka makes an excellent base for fruit infusions or liqueurs as it has a neutral taste and allows the flavour and aroma of the fruit or flowers to take centre stage. I regularly make sloe vodka, cherry vodka, and raspberry vodka for personal consumption and I'll share my blackberry whisky recipe with you here if only to demonstrate the level of difficulty involved. Fill a large screw-top glass jar or two-litre plastic water bottle with cheap own-brand whisky, 200g granulated sugar and 1.4kg of blackberries. Mix it till the sugar dissolves and then store it in a cool dark place, shaking it once every couple of days for two weeks. Strain it through muslin and bottle. Ready to drink right away and fabulous for after-shooting parties, evening barbeques or après ski!

Meat and meat products

Meat and meat products are not surprisingly among the principal earners for smallholders up and down the country. But given the risk of spreading contagious illnesses such as bovine TB, mad cow disease and foot and mouth and the danger to human health posed by the various forms of food poisoning, meat production is also, equally unsurprisingly, among the most regulated businesses in the country.

Perhaps the most contentious and certainly the most emotive issue in meat production is the actual slaughter itself. This is, mercifully, not something you will be called upon or even allowed to do: see the preceding chapter for details. You will, however, have to register as a food business (see below); and although the Retail Butcher's Licence introduced in May 2000 after the last serious FMD outbreak was abolished in 2006 when new EU regulations came into force, there is still an awful lot you need to know if you plan to handle and sell exposed (i.e. unpackaged) raw meat. Find out what you need to know – and how much you don't know – at **www.food.gov.uk/business-industry/caterers/food-hygiene/butchers**, after which you might feel the need for proper training. If so, visit **www.foodtraining.org.uk**. These sites are also invaluable in helping you to assemble a list of the equipment and consumables you are going to need, without which you can't make proper costings.

Planning permission might also be an issue. As cutting and packaging are ancillary to your main business of stockrearing you don't need planning permission to carry out the activities themselves, but there may be issues such as noise, smell and traffic movements for which you do need permission from the district council's planning or building control department.

Other issues for discussion with different departments of your district council include the internal layout and equipment of your cutting and packing rooms (Environmental Health); regulations regarding packaging and labelling (Trading Standards Department); and business rates (Finance Department). This last is a tricky one. Straightforward agricultural land and buildings such as barns and tractor-sheds are exempt, but diversification sometimes crosses the line and becomes eligible. As every case is unique and every council seems to have a different interpretation of the law, you may well find yourself calling on the services of a specialist surveyor. In the meantime Farmers Weekly will explain the broad outlines at **www.fwi.co.uk**.

Finally, causing pollution through the discharge of sewage or other effluents including those from animal sheds and processing units is a criminal offence. Since this is another occasion where every case is unique, then you really need to head off trouble by consulting your water and sewerage provider and the Environment Agency beforehand. The Agency has a nine-page PDF on its website **www.gov.uk/ea** giving guidance on how to complete form B6 (application for an environmental permit – water-discharge activity). Contact your local office in person and if possible try to arrange a site visit. These two consultations have a place in planning your costs: the first, with your water and sewerage provider, may well end in a reassessment of its charges or will at least confirm the existing charges; the second may recommend works that you can then get estimates for.

Having dealt with officialdom and put a figure on your compliance costs, it's time to factor in your outlays on feed, housing and bedding, veterinary and welfare bills such as routine worming and shearing, abattoir and butchery, plus packaging and retailing. This is a fairly routine exercise, but it's worth taking into account some of the ways these bills can be reduced. If you nitrogenate spent soil with a rotation of legumes, for instance, remember that broad beans aren't nicknamed horse-beans for nothing – they're fantastically high in protein, and every single bean is a miniature pharmacopeia of minerals and other nutrients. They're susceptible to disease and don't compete well with weeds, but they crop very heavily at five tonnes or more per hectare on most British soils; and any you don't sell to human customers can be dried for an excellent winter feed for most quadrupeds. Hay can also yield five tonnes per hectare, and if you have the equipment to cut your own you can always cut a neighbour's too – for a price, of course.

The by-products of brewing and cidermaking, spent grains and pressed apple pulp or pomace are also excellent feed. Spent grains are actually the ground malt from which the fermentable sugars have been extracted by mashing in warm water and then straining. Most of the maltose sugar will have been leached out of the resulting porridge, but it's still rich in protein and fibre and is perfect as a dietary supplement for all animals from chickens to cattle. You can substitute between 20–40 per cent of the feed ration or give it as an occasional treat, depending on availability, which not only cuts your costs but also improves the flavour of the resulting meat – and a top product will command a top price.

Pomace, the crushed apple and pear pulp left over from your own and or a neighbour's cider and perry making, is another great supplement. Apart from the natural sugar and fibre, pomace contains a good percentage of protein and doesn't require any other preparation before offering as feed as long as it's used fresh: it doesn't keep and attracts insects and rats as well as bacteria and mould spores if left lying around. (However, you can leave a small amount in a quiet space for wildlife. I used to leave the very last cider apples on the trees especially for the redwings, and put out a little pomace for hedgehogs, voles and any other little creatures looking for food in late autumn. Fat voles make happy barn owls!) Food and drink businesses that supply by-products as animal feed have to comply with the EC Feed Hygiene Regulation 183/2005, the Feed (Hygiene and Enforcement) (England) Regulations 2005, the Food Safety and Hygiene (England) Regulations 2013 and their Scottish and Irish equivalents. What this rather intimidating list actually boils down to in practice is that to supply pig farmers or others with pomace or spent grains as feed, you have to register with the county council and draw up a Hazard Analysis Critical Control Point plan to ensure the safety of the feed. You'll be issued with a registration number and may be inspected periodically (although we never were!).

Now you've established your costs, your next task is market research, in particular the price your product can command and how and where you intend to sell it.

As far as price is concerned, the key thing is to avoid comparison with your mass-produced competitors. Not only do they enjoy vast economies of scale, they can also pad out the prime meat content of pies and sausages and so forth with significant quantities of – well, meat that isn't exactly prime; and in this way they can make a profit on prices of £2.50lb or less. The thing is, though, that to the consumer your products and the supermarket's don't actually look all that different, so it's hard to establish a premium if they're ever displayed side by side.

One place where customers will never be able to compare the price of your steak with that of a supermarket steak is in a restaurant, hotel or pub. They'll certainly appreciate the quality – the tenderness, the texture, the taste – that come from your stockrearing practices and your careful ageing of the meat; and that's why discerning chefs and managers will willingly pay you what your produce is really worth.

You should be able to sell superb joints and other cuts of prime meat in all their naked glory for a suitable premium to the catering trade, but when selling direct to the consumer a golden rule applies: add value. Process the meat yourself, or have it processed for you, and enjoy a commensurately higher profit margin. A joint of meat will fetch less per pound than good meaty sausages or rare breed home-smoked bacon. And customers will be delighted with innovative products such as dry cure Ayrshire bacon or Italian-style pancetta, or luxury stuffings made with pork, apricot and ginger. Some abattoirs have in-house butchers who will produce sausages and bacon from your carcases (but check beforehand what they'll charge!), and I know lots of smallholders who turn whole pigs into sausages, as they sell so well locally and can realise from £5–£10lb. And be imaginative in your approach to retail: don't stop at upscale farm shops or farmers' markets: you can sell uncooked meat and even fish products perfectly safely via social media these days, and you could go retro and reinvent meat clubs and raffles at your local pub.

One message that will distance you from mass-market competitors is that British farm welfare standards are among the best in the world, and the canny small-scale producer needs to hammer it home ruthlessly. Many shoppers don't realise that most supermarket meat is reared outside the UK, often in jurisdictions where welfare standards can be poor. Your website and social media can be filled with pictures of happy animals in sylvan settings, leading happy lives and having quick and pain-free processing. By waving the British-bred, locally-reared flag small producers can ensure higher prices.

Starting a smokery

Sausages and bacon are the perhaps the processed meats with which the public most strongly associates the smallholder. But smoked food is rising in popularity in the UK, perhaps because our tastes are becoming more exotic; and what used to be seen as an old-fashioned method of food preservation is very fashionable now. And we're not just talking about smoked salmon and smoked bacon here but various fish including trout, cod, eels and oysters, cheeses, poultry, charcuterie, garlic – even smoked mead!

There are two methods: hot and cold smoking. Hot smoking over a bed of charcoal and wood chips in a kiln both slow-cooks and flavours the product, so is commonly used for meat and fish. Cold smoking entails putting the product in an unheated chamber and pumping aromatic smoke through it for 12-48 hours. The smoke can be generated by oak, hickory, apple or fruitwood chips. You will still need to cook the fish as this process only cures it; the exceptions being salmon and oysters, which can both be eaten straight from the smoker.

Starting off with a few products you've practised making and are happy with, and maybe saving money by fabricating your own equipment, this is a potentially profitable way to process and add value to your own produce. Courses are available all over the UK, but a good place to start is **www.smokyjos.co.uk**.

Nuts and edible seeds

There is a vast market in the UK for nuts, seeds and dried fruit, much of which is imported but could easily be produced in the UK, creating a niche market for the artisan producer. The UK is eminently suitable for the culture of hazel and cobnuts, some walnut varieties, sweet chestnuts and seed mixes. As well as the lucrative Christmas market for nuts there is also a market for healthy snack food, home baking supplies and breakfast mixes.

By targeting marketing at parents keen to replace sweet snacks with healthier options and young professionals looking for healthy, nutritious snacks, as well as traditional markets, the producer can reach a larger market. At the moment older consumers make up the bulk of the market for nuts, with young professional women preferring seeds and seed mixes. Highlighting the British origin of nuts and seeds and the reduction of food miles and possible contamination of foreign products could be the key to persuading consumers to seek out British produce. Adding value, as always, will bring the price up, so think honey-roasted nuts, and chilli, yoghurt or chocolate-coated nuts, and small quantities in well priced-bags (£1 or £2) or attractive gift boxes at higher prices.

Hazelnuts grow wild in all parts of the UK, with the cultivated varieties mainly grown in the south eastern counties of England. Cobnuts (*Corylus avellana*) have a short papery frill or husk at the base of the nut. These are the more commonly produced nut in the UK. Filberts (*Corylus maxima*) have a longer husk that covers the nut. They will tolerate shade and are wind-pollinated, with male and female flowers on the same tree. A mix of varieties will ensure better pollination as will planting to avoid frost pockets. Planting 2–3 metres apart in rows 4–5 metres apart will allow good machine access.

Nut trees start cropping in their third year and can be harvested in September when the husks yellow. Stored in trays or nets in a dry, airy and rat-proof room or shed and they will keep for up to a year. Full harvest at around eight years can produce 3.5 tonnes per hectare.

Good productive varieties include C. *maxima* 'Kentish Cob' (also called Lambert's Filbert just to be confusing), C. *maxima* 'Gunslebert', and C. *maxima* 'Butler'. Netting is necessary to protect against squirrels.

Walnuts are not indigenous to the UK, and consequently we tend to import them from Asia and the US. However, a sunny wind-protected site with trees planted nine metres apart will provide a good harvest (300kg per acre) in seven years. Walnuts are a very common crop in the Perigord area of southwestern France, where the nuts drop when ripe and are dried for six months to a year before being either sold or pressed for oil. Varieties that perform well in the UK include Juglans Fernor and J. Lara. Leave a substantial distance between walnuts and other cropping trees because its roots produce a toxic substance called Juglone, which can affect the growth of other species. This distance can be up to four times the height of the tree. Unfortunately the English climate does not always guarantee enough warmth to produce fully-formed nuts, but you can always pick them unripe for pickling. The process takes around three weeks and produces a wonderful delicacy served with cheese and cold meats.

Sweet chestnuts (*Castanea sativa*) are only suitable for sandy, acid soils and they too develop into large trees. Fabulous for timber and for edible nuts this species is developing a niche market in the UK, and the fruit are perfect for roast chestnuts, exotic stuffing mixes and deliciously sinful marrons glacés. France has successfully hybridised varieties and C. *Belle epin* and C. *Marigoule* crop at five years old. These new varieties are pest and disease resistant and crop more heavily with a better flavour than wild trees. For more information on nuts visit **www.agroforestry.co.uk**.

Pumpkin and sunflower seeds can be produced easily in the UK and processed as snack or health foods or used by bakeries as an additive to bread. Edible poppy seed from *Papaver somniferum* are also used by bakers. Millet is becoming popular as a tasty snack.

Seaweed

Although seaweed has been collected and used both as a foodstuff as a soil improver and other uses for centuries, there was no attempt to

Case study
Ron and Judith Gillies, Cairn o'Mhor Wines, East Inchmichael Farm, Errol, Perthshire
www.cairnomohr.com

Ron and Judith have been making fruit wines and cider since 1987, having come from very different backgrounds. Judith was actually a doctor, while Ron used to make garden sheds with his brother on the family steading. His two older brothers run a traditional arable farmstead at East Inchmichael, and Cairn o'Mhor rents its buildings from them.

It all started when Ron and Judith got a book on winemaking and started experimenting. After some reasonably good efforts they decided to turn their hobby into a small business making around 3,000 bottles a year – just enough to cover their costs – in a shed. Today, in a bespoke winery built in 1994, annual production exceeds 300,000 bottles, and the winery is not only Scotland's oldest, but also its largest.

The fruit they use comes from different sources. Most of it is either grown on site, where they have planted a small elder orchard, or bought in from local growers; but much of it is foraged among the hedgerows and fields within a 25-mile radius of the farm. The range comprises 20 fruit wines and a cider: the Gillies pressed 50 tonnes of apples in 2016 on state-of-the-art German mills and belt presses. Most of the wines are between 11–13% ABV and are aged for at least a year and they also produce non-alcoholic wines. The fruit wines are all made in the traditional and proper way of fermentation followed by at least a year of maturation. This gives the wines real vinosity and smooth, well-developed flavours

They started with a core range of five types; strawberry, raspberry, bramble, elderberry and oak leaf, then added the sparkling oak and elder for their own wedding followed by the sparkling strawberry for another wedding. The business employs 15 staff.

Social media is a big part of Cairn o'Mhor's marketing with Facebook (10,000 followers), Twitter, Instagram and YouTube accounts all in regular use. The winery also has a strong following on TripAdvisor, mainly due to its summer tours and cafe. A big draw for visitors is that Ron likes to share his slightly quirky lifestyle with them and they love it. He has understood and exploited the fact that people love a story and keep coming back for more. Yes, he makes a tasty product, but it's the lifestyle they are buying into. There's no hard-sell on his website or social media: it's all a bit of fun and as a result, people are buying his product in droves.

assess production volume until 2013, when the wild seaweed (or sea vegetables) harvest was estimated at around 2,000–3,000 dry tonnes. Red seaweeds including laverbread, carrageen and dulce are used as food and a condiment; and many of the green types are used in soups, sauces and as a flavour enhancer. The market in sea vegetables is growing at a rate of 7–10 per cent annually, with Europe being one of the largest consumers. The main drivers are increasing demand for Asian food and growing awareness of the health benefits. Trials conducted on the west coast of Scotland indicate a potential annual crop of 24 tonnes per hectare. Visit **www.seaveg.uk/seaweed-farming**.

Polytunnels

A polytunnel will lengthen your growing season and allow you to grow warm-weather crops you might otherwise struggle with, including grapes, peppers, chillies and cut flowers. Alternatively you might want to focus on producing year-round salad crops – tomatoes, cucumbers, chard, leaves of all sorts, herbs; another option is to exploit the controlled climate of the tunnel to produce out-of-season French beans, asparagus, courgettes and other favourites. Then there are also exotics like wasabi or Japanese horseradish for which you might find trade customers.

One of the best-yielding and highest-value options for your polytunnels is soft fruit. Raspberries, strawberries, redcurrants, blackcurrants and blueberries all command high prices both fresh and frozen. Less common soft fruits include whitecurrants, loganberries, tayberries and gooseberries. Soft fruit production can be field-based on sheltered sites in southern and southwestern counties where there is a mild climate and good free-draining soil; elsewhere, polytunnels and old-school glasshouses make it possible too. Soft fruits are incredibly versatile: many supermarket chains like to source them locally (as they do with salads and other delicate produce) provided you can satisfy some fairly onerous supplier criteria and live with their prices. Imperfect fruit can be sold to makers of yoghurt, soft drinks, soft desserts and ice-cream (and of course you may well be making your own) and then there's always the country wines we mentioned above. The tunnel itself can be pretty versatile too: it's normally out of use for growing in late winter/early spring, just when you want a large, airy, but easy-to-heat lambing shed. (You can put a washing line up in a polytunnel, too!)

The entry price starts at less than £200 for a domestic-sized tunnel if you want to try your hand at growing before making the big investment; an 18′ x 90′ commercial-sized tunnel can be yours for £2,000 or thereabouts; with the larger sizes you will also probably need mechanical pickers, washing plant, refrigeration and on-site packaging to ensure the quickest possible transit from harvesting to the shelf. The price depends on your ambitions, but most of what you need is available second-hand and reconditioned. Do check with your district council's planning department about the size, siting and permanency of polytunnels before committing to any spending, though: different councils have different attitudes as to whether tunnels are exempt from planning control or are a blight on the landscape to be stopped at all costs, however indirect or underhand.

Edible flowers

The UK cut flower market has altered to take advantage of increased demand for woody ornamentals, wild flowers and varieties that would never have been seen in high street florists 20 years ago. The importation mainly from Holland of cheap and plentiful supplies has only just started to be challenged because of a rise in prices, recognition of the value of home-grown British blooms and a change of fashion. However, another blossoming market is quickly gaining momentum in the UK, and that is edible flower production.

Edible flowers are more and more frequently found in restaurants, bars, cafes and now high-class food stores, and there's a large variety available. From borage and other herbs frozen into ice-cubes for designer drinks, saffron from the British saffron crocus (*Crocus sativus*) and colourful blooms for chefs to sprinkle on salads, the edible flower is here to stay. The use of glasshouses and polytunnels means they can be grown virtually year-round, and national distribution channels are well-established.

Saffron in particular is gaining popularity among growers, especially as the strands or dried stigmas can command up to £60 for 80. One flower can produce three stigmas, so a lot of bulbs are required for meaningful production, and corms can be divided when bulking up, usually every four or five years to replant as new plants. They flower in autumn and prefer warm silty soils.

Registering a food business

To carry out any kind of food operation, including selling, cooking, storing, handling, preparing or distributing food, you must register your business with your district council at least 28 days before starting up. You are required to register every premises where you carry out food operations, including your home and all mobile or temporary premises such as stalls and vans. It doesn't cost anything to register and your registration can't be refused.

If you make, prepare or handle food that comes from animals, for example meat or dairy products, other than for direct sale to the public, your premises may need to be approved by the council before you can undertake the activity. Check the Food Premises Approval sections if you think that this applies to you:

- Food Premises Approval (England)
- Food Premises Approval (Northern Ireland)
- Food Premises Approval (Scotland)
- Food Premises Approval (Wales)

If you are approved you don't need to register as well. You may be fined, imprisoned for up to two years or both if you run a food business without registering. Further information on starting up a new food business is available from the Food Standards Agency **www.gov-uk/food**.

The orchard

06

An orchard has the potential to produce a really substantial profit, depending on what you plant and what you do with it, and apples are one of the easiest fruits to grow. But there's more to an orchard than that. There's something very rewarding about plucking a ripe, sun-warmed apple from a tree you planted and nurtured and watched blossom, and whose tiny fruits you observed as they swelled and coloured, weighing the branches down with honeyed sweetness. And there's something timeless about the passage of the seasons in an orchard, marking family occasions there from christenings to weddings and even commemorating the passing of a loved one with the planting of a tree. Taking your youngster to hospital after that first fall out of a tree; closing your eyes in your deckchair and drifting off to the drowsy buzzing of honeybees in the blossom; clearing up after that memorable impromptu wassail. Oh yes, happy memories.

And at the same time, you are almost literally watching money grow on trees.

The most versatile of crops

Apples come in five types and thousands of varieties. There are dessert apples (eaters), culinary apples (cookers), cider apples, crab apples and wildings. There are commercial varieties grown by the hundreds of tonnes for their sweetness, low acidity, pest and disease resistance and keeping qualities; and there are local heritage varieties, gnarly little pachyderms, unlovely on the eye but with an unmatched flavour, only to be found in one or two orchards up a twisting green lane. Think about your customers, your marketing and your potential outlets. If you want to sell your produce at the farm gate or in local greengrocers' shops or at farmers' markets, make yourself stand out with those heritage varieties rather than the common-or-garden supermarket stuff. By all means contract-grow in bulk for wholesalers, but selling direct to the consumer carries a higher margin.

Planting cookers? There is more choice than just Bramleys. Bramleys may be popular with shoppers, who at least recognise the name;

but from the grower's point of view they're notorious for scab and canker, especially when grown in western counties, and you want a trouble-free orchard if possible. Again, seek out local heritage varieties that will attract both keen home cooks and professional chefs with an eye for the unusual.

Want dessert apples all year round? Plant an early and a medium or a late-cropping eater and you'll have table fruit from August until spring: earlies don't keep well, but late-season apples, properly stored in a dry cellar or loft, will last until late spring or even early summer. Do be careful about varieties, though: modern eaters like Gala and Jazz aren't actually much sweeter than old favourites like Coxes and Worcesters but they are much, much less acidic, and it's to be feared that modern shoppers have lost the taste for that sharp acidity that goes so well with a well-matured British hard cheese.

Can't use up or sell your whole crop? Then juice it, and what you don't sell as delicious fresh juice you can always turn into cider. Contrary to myth, cider can be made with any old apples, and in eastern and southeastern England it is. But if you really fancy cidermaking as a serious business then you will want some cider apple trees too. It's the balance of sugar, acid and tannins that determines which category a strain of apple falls into: cider apples are either bittersweet or bittersharp. They are also structurally different from dessert apples, having a more robust internal cell structure which helps release the juice during pressing; and in the main they're really quite unpleasant to eat raw. I have very fond memories as a tutor asking my students to familiarise themselves with the taste of Ashton Bitters. If you've never bitten into a real cider apple, then the taste is similar to chewing a wet teabag.

And finally, a crab apple tree will aid pollination and provide a crop of tart fruit that can produce jams and jellies. Make sure it's a proper crab: the little green apples you find in hedges are as often as not wildings. Apple strains are all cloned and don't breed true: left to themselves over the generations these are what they revert too. Wildings aren't much good for anything except verjus – thin, sharp, preferably unripe juice used as an alternative to vinegar – or a rather acidic mulch that will benefit most fruits.

Establishing an orchard

The benefits of orchards are many, and I would urge any smallholder to establish one or, if you already have trees, to maintain and exploit them. From planting to harvesting, a half-decent crop can take five to seven years, depending on the rootstock of the tree itself and the location, altitude, average rainfall and aspect of your orchard and the quality, depth and moisture content of its soil; getting it right first time and avoiding having to repeat the whole business later on involves taking all these variables into account. Because every orchard really is different: in mine, in Cornwall, the wind was predominantly from the southwest, straight off the Atlantic, but I could get a vicious north wind too so it needed a good shelter belt. And it had its quirks, which I discovered as I went along. While planting up gaps in my shelter belt one day I was digging a hole for an ash sapling, and when I got down a foot or so it started to back-fill with water. I had discovered our high water table! I filled the gap with hazel bushes instead: they don't mind the wet so much, they're maintenance-free, they provide good straight pea and bean poles and as a bonus they supplied the nuts for my Christmas cheeseboard.

Planting

Nearly all apple varieties available today are the result of one or other of the ancient processes of grafting or budding. Apples are almost all clones and don't breed true, so if you grow one from seed you will probably end up with something that is nothing like its parent at all. To ensure you get the variety you want tape, a budding branch or scion cut from your chosen tree into a nick cut in a suitable rootstock or host. This operation, known as grafting, is carried out in spring. The rootstock comprises the rootball of the host tree with a trunk or stem long enough to stand around six inches proud of the soil when planted. Your choice of rootstock determines the vigour and size of the adult tree, and also in some cases bestows some disease resistance. Budding is a similar operation carried out in July and August and using a single bud rather than a scion. Grafting and budding are simple but very delicate operations: there are countless pages on the internet, some with diagrams, others with videos, that will show you exactly how they're done. What's common to them both is that all-important rootstock.

I have grown mainly from MM106 stock that produces half-standards that aren't unmanageably large at harvest and pruning time. How densely to plant depends on how good the soil, aspect and shelter are (apple trees are prone to root damage from windrock and do need shelter belts). A quarter of an acre might support as many as 75 trees on MM106 rootstock, which as you can see from the table below adds up to an awful lot of apples! It adds up to quite a lot of money, too: with rootstocks at £2.25–£3 and upward each, and lengths of scionwood at £4 each for fairly run-of-the-mill varieties online from companies like Amelia's Apples. Another consideration regarding the density of planting is how to cope with all that fruit: how to get it all picked (especially if you grow the larger M25s), how to store it all, process it all and sell it all. So before you start buying your trees, get the calculator out and do your sums!

In the table facing I've listed a few of the more common UK rootstocks with their particular attributes. However, the grower needs to bear in mind that the individual circumstances of each orchard will affect the overall size the trees will achieve; they will probably never reach their full potential if the soil is shallow and dry and the landscape is windswept.

Measure all spacings from stem to stem. If planting several trees, mark the spacings on the ground with a bamboo or hazel stick before you dig the holes. If you have existing trees or a hedge, start measuring at least five metres away: they will have extensive root systems of their own that will compete with your new trees.

Using these figures as a guide you can see that a plot measuring 10m x 10m can fit four MM106s or one M25. Certain varieties, especially if they're triploids, may be more vigorous and need a little more room than your average tree. If in doubt have an in-depth talk with the nursery supplying the rootstock and scions.

You should by now have an idea of what types and even what

Table Rootstock explanation

Rootstock	M27	M9	M26
Ultimate height	1 – 2m	2 – 3m	2.9 – 3.5m
Soil	Good, deep, fertile soil. Permanent stake. No competition.	Good, deep, fertile soil, permanent stake. No competition.	Good, deep, fertile soil. Stake for 5 years. Growing in grass will slow growth.
Spacing	5 – 6ft 1.5 – 1.8m	5 – 6ft 1.5 – 1.8m	10ft 3m
Years to fruiting	2 – 3 yrs	2 – 3 yrs	3 – 4 yrs
Uses	Cordon, patio tree, Patio / pots	Cordon, step over, bush. Small garden.	Cordon, step over, espalier, bush. Med garden.
Yield at 10 yrs	7kg	20kg	30kg

Rootstock	MM106	MM111	M25
Ultimate height	3.5 – 5.m	4.5 – 6m	6.5 – 9m
Soil	Can tolerate heavier soils & exposed conditions. Can be grown in grass. Remove stake after 5 years.	Tolerates most soils & conditions. Grows in grass. Remove stake after 5 years.	Most soils & conditions. Good pest/disease resistance. Grows in grass or hedge. Remove stake after 5 years.
Spacing	12ft 3.6m	22 – 25ft 7-8m	25 – 30ft 7.6-9m
Years to fruiting	3 – 4 yrs	5 – 6 yrs	6 – 7 yrs
Uses	Espalier, fan, bush, half standard. Med-large garden, schools.	Standard. Community orchard, farm/traditional orchard. Replaces MM106 in challenging areas.	Standard. Farm/traditional orchard
Yield at 10 yrs	50kg	90kg	120kg

varieties will best suit your business plan, so take a mental walk round the plot and place them. You might want to keep all your eaters close together and your cooking or cider apples separate. Bear in mind that you want flowering groups close to or overlapping each other to optimise pollination. Your choice of rootstock is equally important: dwarf, standard, half standard, pot-grown or bare-root. Bare-root will be available in the dormant season, meaning you will only be able to plant from January till March; pot-grown can be bought and planted at any time of year. Personally I prefer bare-rooted trees because they're supplied at either one or two years old and therefore establish more quickly than pot-grown. They're usually cheaper, too!

Funding

Despite years of austerity there is still some funding available for planting orchards, but the various schemes tend to be linked to ecology and the environment and their aims and requirements don't necessarily chime with yours. As I write there are orchard grants available through The People's Trust for Endangered Species. The grant is for standard trees only, i.e. on M25 or MM111 rootstocks, so it may not suit you; but check out **www.ptes.org/orchard-grants**. It's available to private landowners and community orchards. Natural England also funds traditional fruit trees of various species as part of its hedgerow management countryside stewardship scheme. Trees must be on M25 and planted in hedgerows, and there are myriad other rules; if you're interested visit **www.gov.uk/countryside-stewardship-grants/planting-fruit-trees**. Look also at the Farming and Wildlife Advisory Group www.fwag.org.uk and LEADER funding, **www.gov.uk/government/organisations/rural-development-programme-for-england-network** and **www.ruralnetwork.scot/funding/leader**.

Grants like these that only support traditional standard orchards may present management problems for growers, but such orchards are undoubtedly havens for all sorts of wildlife. We can't all plant orchards entirely with standard trees, but even one or two planted among the semi-standards offer food and shelter to many insect, bird and rodent species. Standards also live longer and therefore provide a more stable habitat than short-lived commercial orchards, which also tend towards over-reliance on fertiliser, pesticides and herbicides. Careful choice of rootstock and variety and good pruning (see below) eliminates the need for fertiliser and pesticides altogether, and grass orchards need only occasional cutting or can be undergrazed (see below). Surrounding the orchard with diverse hedging will further encourage birds, butterflies, hedgehogs, bats and owls that all contribute to the creation of an idyllic retreat that will refresh and gladden the heart and which changes with the seasons.

Incidentally, I never applied for organic status for my orchard as I objected to the high costs and the length of time it took to get accreditation (see Chapter 10). But I didn't use any chemicals in the orchard at all, not fertiliser, not pesticides, not herbicides. I cut the grass to a manageable sward and left the clippings to break down naturally. I pruned out and burnt any dead or cankered twigs and kept the orchard clean and tidy. As a result I had a thriving orchard with butterflies and moths, bats and barn owls. And as the orchard matured, birds and animals deposited wildflower seeds, bringing more insects and hence more birds. I couldn't sell my ciders as organic, but they were as natural as it's possible to be.

Scions for sale

The trees themselves generate a ready supply of scionwood to use for your own grafting or to sell on to other growers. Cutting scions in early spring can be incorporated into your pruning regime. Imagine – people paying for the parts of the tree you would normally use for kindling!

When selecting scionwood, look for straight twigs of the current season's growth, about pencil thickness with visible but flattish buds. Make sure they're disease-free and cut them about 5–6" long. Some old-fashioned varieties are very spindly and you'll have to search for the thickest twigs you can find. If you're sending them through the post, wrapping fresh-cut scions in wet newspaper will keep them viable. They will store for a few days wrapped in clingfilm in the fridge.

Taking this idea further, you could also produce your own rootstocks for grafting and budding by establishing a small nursery bed for the purpose. I stuck with MM106 because the trees on maturity were a good but not outlandish height; I didn't need specialist equipment to collect the fruit, and they were quite disease-resistant and cropped fairly quickly. I used to have long portions of rootstock cut off that I would either plant direct into the nursery bed or into a large pot filled with a 50:50 mix of earth and compost. I could increase my stock even more by cutting them in half, although to no less than 30cm. I'd push half the length into the soil (right way up), water it in well and leave it for about four months to root in an area protected from rabbits and deer and kept free of weeds. When the cuttings started to look firm and alive, possibly with leaves beginning to appear, I would gently pull any that looked dubious. If they hadn't rooted they would lift straight away, but if they had they would resist my pulling. The rooted stocks would be ready to use or sell the following spring or the year after if I wanted more root growth.

You can also produce young apple trees to sell on. With the ability to grow your own rootstocks and harvest appropriate scion material, you can produce local or heritage varieties for which there is a small but discerning market. A nice potted two-year-old tree of a heritage or local variety on MM106 will easily fetch £20-£30, and as you already produce the rootstock and the scion you will only have to lay out for pots and growing medium.

Pruning and maintenance

Choosing disease and pest resistant varieties limits maintenance work more or less to pruning and preparing for the harvest. Pruning the shaggy tops of the trees during their winter dormancy is an essential preparation for the growing season: it lets in light and air to keep the fruit dry and healthy and full of energy, and directs the vigour of the tree into its more productive branches. In the north and Scotland, winter pruning is carried out between December and early March; in Cornwall the window is much tighter as it is not cold enough for true dormancy until January, and the task must be completed before mid-February.

Winter pruning can be as simple or as complicated as you want. Personally, I removed any dead, diseased or damaged twigs or branches and then gently shaped the tree into an open goblet form in my traditional orchard. If you plan to grow more intensively and on a larger scale, then pruning has to be regimented to ensure that picking machinery can easily and quickly move between rows of trees, and any ground cover is usually weed-killed to prevent competition for nutrients. Pruned material is best removed and burnt, unless you have enough to make it worth turning into charcoal, which is not only a wonderful fuel but shines equally as a soil conditioner. Add the Christmas tree and wreath to the kiln to bulk it out and the combined scents of pine resin and applewood make a divine barbecue fuel.

Another routine task best carried out during dormancy includes removing branches that are rubbing. This will leave a large open surface that presents less risk of infection during dormancy than it would in the growing season. Recent research shows that the traditional option of treating the cut surface with wound paint of any variety ancient or modern can do more harm than good, so any maintenance that involves the use of the saw had best be done in winter. During the early growing season you can also pinch out some of the fruit-buds in a cluster that looks too tight for the health of the individual fruit, and you can carry on pinching out throughout summer to make sure the apples get a good current of air to keep them dry and free of spores and mites.

Late frosts

Few misfortunes can break your heart like a really sharp late frost. At bedtime your trees are a froth of fine, healthy, glowing white blossom. During the night the temperature plummets, and you rush out anxiously next morning to inspect the damage. To your relief there appears to be none – the blossoms are as pristine as when you last saw them yesterday afternoon. But as the day wears on they seem to sicken, to lose their bloom, to discolour and wither away. The frost has killed them.

This is no threat to the trees. They overproduce blossom on a heroic scale against just such an eventuality, and enough will survive to ensure their continuation. But the handful of mature fruits that will satisfy the trees' reproductive urge is worthless to you, and it might seem that there is nothing you can do but shrug and sigh and hope for better next year. However, there are steps you can take to mitigate the disaster.

First, pay close attention to the weather forecast from the moment your buds begin to unfurl until the fruit is set. If you have mulched your trees, or if sheep have kept the grass short, the earth immediately around the trunks should be all but bare. When a deep frost is forecast then go out as long before nightfall as possible, rake any mulch away, and give the soil a really good soak with a hose. This will turn the earth itself into a night storage heater, radiating the warmth it has soaked up through the day upwards and increasing the temperature among the branches by a good 2–3C.

If the forecast is very severe, and provided your trees are small enough and indeed few enough, you can augment the night-storage effect by throwing a sheet of horticultural fleece over them, spread wide to capture as much of the earth's warmth as possible. But that's really only feasible in a garden. On a larger scale, you can deploy lawn-sprinklers to build up a sheath of protective ice over the buds. If done slowly enough, much of the warmth given up by the water as it freezes, will spread into the twigs and flowers, and the layer of ice will trap it there until morning.

Undergrazing

Traditional orchards are natural pastures that can produce much more than just apples. The orchard can be undergrazed by chickens, lambs, goats and other poultry and livestock that will not only keep the grass short and nibble off bramble shoots as they appear – both of which make harvesting your apples immeasurably quicker and easier – but will also nitrogenate the soil making for healthier trees and, if you're a cidermaker, a faster and more reliable fermentation. If you don't fatten lambs of your own you might be able to rent your orchard out as summer keep to someone who does.

Case Study
Dorset Nectar Cider, Bridport
www.dorsetnectar.co.uk

Oliver and Penny Strong didn't originally set out to make cider. In fact, Oliver was looking for a home for his metal sculpting business when in 2006 he bought two off-grid agricultural barns that came with a 15-acre cider apple orchard and some equipment.

The Strongs had previous experience in farming, horticulture and running a business and were keen to try something new, so they ended the holding's contract with Gaymers and started making cider themselves. With no formal training, they got hands-on experience from other cidermakers such as Rose Grant of Cider by Rosie fame, and theoretical knowledge from books by Alan Stone, Liz Copas, Andrew Lea and Peter Mitchell.

Having invested all their money in the site and equipment, they had nothing left to spend on a family home off-site, so they took a huge risk and built themselves a small cabin in the orchard. There followed a hard battle with West Dorset District Council for retrospective planning permission, which was finally granted on appeal in 2013.

The orchard has around 3,000 45-year-old trees, mainly bitter-sweet varieties such as Browns, Dabinett, Coate Jersey, Chesil Jersey, Sweet Coppin, Porter's Perfection and a French variety, Nehou, which all have a high level of tannins to give the cider a rounded and complex flavour. Most of the trees are semi-standard, with a few rows of bush trees and only a handful of M25 standards. The annual yield is around 120 tonnes. Dorset Nectar gained organic status in 2011.

The Strongs produce their cider in the traditional way, pressing the fruit on two large hydraulic rack and cloth rigs and fermenting the juice with natural airborne yeasts, although it's not sold at natural strength but watered down to 4% ABV. They also cater for the current vogue for flavoured ciders.

The family – four of them are now working for the company – has taken a great deal of care over marketing and customer relations. With a website, social media presence, an excellent competition record, meet the producer tastings and national newspaper coverage, the business is steadily growing. They currently produce ten varieties of cider and intend to expand their orchard size, update machinery and increase product range to include vinegars, champagne ciders and apple brandy. They have now started to export to the Netherlands as well.

Dorset Nectar produces 98% of its income from cider, apple juice and cider vinegar, with a small secondary income from bottling and filtering for other cider makers.

Either way, choose the right grasses and plant plenty of meadow flowers that will improve the grass's flavour and even the health of the lambs. Different grasses and legumes all have their own special characteristics and the choice of which seeds to sow, and in what proportion, depends on soil and drainage – timothy grass flourishes on heavier soils and makes good hay; sainfoin and lucerne are deep-rooted and do well in dry conditions; all sorts of fescue will tolerate shade; bluegrass and red clover are trample-resistant and can be planted in areas of heavy traffic in gateways and around feeding and water troughs. There's a lot to know, but your seed merchant will probably get you started by offering a proprietary blend suited to your orchard. Watch carefully how each grass flourishes (or otherwise) and re-seed accordingly.

One thing you can and should do to improve the quality of the forage and the health and wellbeing of your livestock (and its marketability) is add the right wildflowers. They're nutritious and, in some cases, medicinal: bird's foot trefoil inhibits the growth of intestinal worms in sheep while narrow-leaved or English plantain has antibiotic qualities. Others you could plant include field and devil's-bit scabious, prunella vulgaris (or self heal), lady's bedstraw, meadowsweet, betony and sage (for which the bees, too, will thank you). Some of these flowers are also nitrogen fixers, which will help to nourish the rest of your forage and your trees as well.

However, there are some caveats. Livestock can and do damage the trees and make a quagmire of the soil. There are some animals you simply can't keep in an orchard, and you have to take firm measures to protect your trees from determined nibblers and gougers that really, really want to get at them. Whatever grazing stock you decide to fatten on your orchard, invest in really substantial tree-guards. If you have enough space to breed sheep or keep goats, then plant full-sized standard M25 rootstocks whose canopies, when grown, will be out of their reach; but you will still need to provide substantial tree-guards for the first 15 years or so. Geese will get their long necks through or above all but the most substantial tree guards and strip young trees of their bark, killing them in the process. Pigs, even the small and allegedly non-rooting breeds such as Kune Kune and Vietnamese Pot Belly, will dig around the trees, destroying roots, bulldozing tree guards and generally reducing your picturesque orchard to firewood. Horses can do similarly catastrophic damage.

The harvest

The most difficult period in the apple-grower's year is the harvest, not just because the work itself is hard but also because it takes a great deal of organising and nature itself isn't necessarily all that co-operative.

Organising the harvest will have started right back when you decided what varieties to plant because they all crop at different times. The earliest cider apples, Morgan Sweet, can ripen as early as July and their cider can be ready for Christmas. By and large, though, depending on the season's growing conditions (and every year is different!) as well the varieties you've chosen, apples start ripening in August and carry on until early December. Modern dessert varieties such as Katy and Discovery are early ripeners that don't keep well and must either be processed or put into cold storage as soon as they are picked. Cider varieties tend to ripen from mid-October onwards, though, so we picked, juiced and fermented our Discovery, Katy, Spartan and Tom Putt first. They would ferment quite quickly as the temperature was still quite high in September, and we used the resulting cider to blend with the more tannic juice of the later varieties which we picked as they ripened. In Cornwall we would normally have finished by the first week in December, but in France there are apples still unharvested at Christmas.

You'll know when each variety is ready to test for ripeness because it will start dropping full-sized windfalls. You will already have been through the early drop when the trees sacrifice surplus fruits in order to help the rest survive to full maturity. The early droppers can be raked up for compost or simply left to rot as mulch and soil improver. When you start getting mature windfalls, though, it's time to start gently pulling the higher-growing fruits, perhaps with a little twist. If its skin feels slightly oily, it comes away cleanly from the wood and its pips are brown, then it's fully ripe and picking can begin. You can use windfalls in cider provided you get to them before they start to rot (the odd bruise doesn't matter), but don't use them in unprocessed juice as they may have been infected by patulin (see below). Even in fully ripe apples not all the starch will have been saccharified (turned to sugar); you can help the process along by storing them for a while in dry heaps or tumps somewhere sheltered from rain and frost but with free-flowing air.

Picking apples in the late autumn sun sounds idyllic, doesn't it? Well it isn't. Autumn may be the season mists and mellow fruitfulness but it's also the season of wasps, slugs, mud and grass that is always long and wet and slippery. It's usually raining, and the days get shorter and colder. The work is backbreaking, and when you're picking all day on your own it can get very lonely as well. The ideal is to acquire a mechanical harvesting rig-out, but with the cheapest tractor-mounted tree shaker costing nearly £2,000 and mechanical harvesters starting at three times that you need either a pretty big orchard to earn back the expense, or second-hand kit (which can turn out more expensive in the end unless you're a bit of a mechanic), or to share with other growers, or to hire a contractor, or perhaps to invest in the kit and set up as a contractor yourself. For the small to medium producer, though, it's hand-picking or no picking at all.

We got help with the picking by advertising on HelpX and Woofers for volunteers. The response came mainly from university students and in autumn East European itinerant workers who came for board, lodging and either pocket-money or the chance to learn how to make cider. We had a caravan big enough for two with its own shower and toilet and asked for six hours' work a day, five days a week. Other growers we knew expected 39 hours' work a week and paid their pickers, but then deducted money for accommodation and food. There is a lot of law you need to know before you employ pickers, though, and a lot of insurance of one sort and another to pay.

There are many methods of picking by hand and although some of them are less toilsome than others, they all qualify as hard labour. Pick as many as possible by hand to avoid bruising and to keep the use of ladders – dangerous things, and slow and cumbersome to boot – to an absolute minimum by planting dwarf or semi-standard rootstock and pruning rigorously. To get at the topmost fruits (and the most stubborn ones!) without doing your back in, keep the ground at the base of trees as bare and as even as possible. Lay down tarpaulins or sheets and shake the trees gently (because they do have quite delicate roots, especially when young) so that the fruits fall on to the tarpaulins that can then be picked up by the corners and emptied into your bags. Use plastic rather than metal rakes to round up any that roll or bounce off the tarpaulin; if your back is a bit dodgy you can pick the apples up with a wide-bladed plastic snowshovel. We used rigid gardening sacks that could carry 100kg to empty the tarpaulins into; when they were almost full two pickers could drag them to a waiting trailer. We also used stacking plastic crates that could hold 25kg each.

From the rootstock chart above you can see how much fruit different sizes of tree might yield in a good year. Of course it differs greatly from variety to variety, and some varieties only crop every other year. But how much is all this fruit worth? Same answer, really: the price of apples varies all over the UK depending on demand and availability. The highest prices at time of writing are about £250 a tonne in Scotland; it gets lower as you go south. The big cidermakers were paying £110–£120 to their contract growers, and in Cornwall we could buy in at around £50 a tonne provided we went and picked it ourselves.

Milling and pressing

It's often said that cider is one of the most ancient alcoholic beverages on Earth, but anyone who has tried to press a worthwhile quantity of apples without the aid of a mechanical press of some sort will tell you that this can't be true; and the lever-press – the first piece of technology capable of pressing apples in large volumes – wasn't documented until about 160BC.

One of the many reasons why our ancient forebears were able to extract the juice or oil from grapes and olives but not from apples in the circular trough mills you still see used in the Mediterranean today is that the apple has much greater compressive strength than the grape or the olive (although even grapes need to have their skins broken either by treading or in an auger before you can press them). Tread on one apple and you'll squash it. Tread on two or three and they'll bear your weight. They have to be ground to a pulp in a mill; and then the pulp has to be squeezed in a press capable of exerting huge pressure before it yields its juice.

Despite the need for not one but two pieces of fairly heavy-duty kit, though, juicing your crop – which is probably going to be what you end up doing with most of it – needn't take much capital outlay.

For small-scale extraction you start with a scratter mill, which is a hopper with revolving blades at the bottom turned either by hand or by a small motor. You can get a brand-new stainless steel 7-litre hand-cranked model for £80–£90 online, perfectly good for extraction on a hobby scale, or an electric-powered version supposedly capable of grinding a tonne of fruit in an hour for less than £300.

The hobbyist's basket-press is, as its name suggests, no more than a box made of wooden slats with a screw-plate on top. A muslin bag stops the pulp from the mill oozing out between the slats while you gradually tighten the screw a few turns at a time. Around the bottom of the box is a gutter in which the juice collects, equipped with a spout under which you have hopefully remembered to put a bucket. These are incredibly laborious and messy: 100-litre versions are available for around £500–600 new, but for production on any sort of scale you'll want something mechanised and therefore more expensive. Expect to pay about £1,000 for a 100-litre hydraulic press, which seems dear but as the equipment is robust (not many moving parts), clean, efficient and cheap to use (the water that fills the pressing bag comes from your tap) it's actually quite good value.

How much juice will you get? Well, it's as long as a piece of string. It depends on the variety of apple, the weather during the growing season and the efficiency of your press. Suffice it to say that the average apple is 70–75 per cent juice by volume and you should be able to extract most of it. If you tump or store your apples in heaps, preferably somewhere dry, for a few days before you press them, evaporation will give you rather less juice while concentration and continuing saccharification (the natural process of starch breaking down into fructose) will make it much sweeter.

Juice

I only used to press enough apple juice for our own household, not for sale to the public, because its commercial appeal was limited then; but fruit juice is a today fast-growing sector in the diversifying small rural business sector that deserves your consideration.

Top fruit and soft fruit are both candidates for juice production and for its twin sister, cordial making. The equipment you need to extract the juice is the same as you would use for cider making, so if you offer one product you can just as easily offer both. However, the regulations governing fruit juice production, storage and sale are slightly more rigorous because, being unfermented and therefore packed with the raw sugar bugs love, fruit juice carries a much higher health and hygiene risk.

Fermentation not only transforms sugar into alcohol, it also generates carbon dioxide, and the combination is lethal to just about every microbe on the planet. But without it, raw fruit juice is a sugary treat and the perfect growth medium for some very nasty bugs indeed, which is why environmental health officers commonly require a white room or similar for bottling raw fruit juices, and why they require you to provide and use a detailed HACCP plan to show due diligence and that you have accounted for every possible source of contamination. I've listed some of them here:

- Moth damage to fruit
- Faecal contamination of the orchard floor (unless you have removed livestock six weeks before harvesting)
- Rodent contamination during fruit storage
- Inadequate fruit grading and washing before pressing
- Inclusion of debris (e.g. insects or glass) in unwashed bottles
- Patulin contamination
- Inefficient pasteurisation of juice during bottling.

Every EHO I've met highlights the risk of patulin whenever

apple or pear juice is mentioned; however we need to keep things in perspective. Patulin is a mycotoxin produced by fungi that grow on fruit. It normally occurs when the fruit has gone mouldy, although spoilage is not always visible. It is possible for patulin to occur inside the fruit if there has been bruising or in apple varieties with an open calyx. Contaminated apple or pear juice usually contains patulin at levels below 50µg/litre, but levels of up to 4,000µg/litre have been reported. Pasteurisation won't destroy it, but the preservative sulphur dioxide often used in fruit juice usually will. Patulin is not normally found in vinegar, cider or perry because yeast destroys it. Sending a small sample from each finished batch of juice for microbial analysis is a cheap way of demonstrating that you have ensured your juice is safe, ticks a box on the HACCP plan and shows due diligence.

Given all this, I would think that the profit margin would be less for juice than that for cider. Production is a lot more involved, but your selling price would be lower than for the same quantity of cider. And as the competition is extremely stiff, you face an uphill struggle to persuade retailers and the public that your juice is different. So interrogate a few independent local retailers before committing yourself to any expenditure: what flavours would they like to see? What market(s) do they think you should be tackling: mature or kids? What sort of packaging do they think appropriate? Only when you have discovered what products they will stock – and got a few firm orders – should you write any cheques.

Cider

After producing cider for ourselves for around five years, we took some advice from our very helpful Environmental Health Officer and went into commercial production on a small scale. Our aim was to make good craft cider from 100 per cent local apple juice and sell it locally. In the main John and I did the pressing, but we had lots of helpers that made it much more fun. By joining the HelpX network (**www.helpx.net**) we found volunteers from Australia, New Zealand, Spain, France, Germany and the USA who wanted to come and work on British farms in exchange for no more than bed and board. It's a great idea and we learned loads from people from a wide variety of backgrounds and cultures. We could never have afforded to take on a seasonal member of staff, but volunteers helped us with some of the bigger jobs on our smallholding. We got help with the heavy work and they got to see Cornwall, so everyone was happy.

In every supermarket the section selling cider is getting bigger and bigger. But if you choose one of the more commercial brands and check the ingredients on the back of the bottle you'll see that the main ingredient isn't apple juice at all but water, followed by sugar or glucose syrup. A proper, REAL, artisan cider is made with 100 per cent apple juice, and artisan cider is growing in popularity with consumers.

And it's a profitable business, too, even on a small scale. Fill in form CP33 or visit **www.tax.service.gov.uk/forms/form/claim-for-exemption-from-registration-by-a-maker-of-cider-or-perry-for-sale/new** to become a duty-exempt producer and make and sell up to 7,000 litres of cider without paying duty or becoming a registered alcohol wholesaler (although that quantity does include cider made for your own use, and the moment you pass 7,000 litres you have to pay duty on your entire output). This exemption has given many cidermakers the opportunity to start small and then either perfect their product and expand or keep the business small and artisanal, supplying a niche product locally. This latter is the approach I took. I wanted to be able to tell my customers what varieties were in each batch, where they came from and how I made it, and to enjoy making my cider instead of having the business run me.

I used apples from around 40 trees of both cider and dessert fruit. At the most I produced 4,000 litres. It was hard work, but I could easily make a good wage from it; and with a ready market locally I didn't even have to think about internet sales. I produced six ciders, which let me hit just about all markets in the area. I made still cider in medium and medium-dry either bottled or bag-in-box – 20L for pubs and 5L for take-home. I also made bottle-conditioned (naturally sparkling) ciders in medium-dry, medium and full bittersweet varieties. My bottled still cider was made without sulphites. (Don't, by the way, use any fruit other than apple or pear or any spices or other flavourings: any of these additives magically and legally transforms your cider into made wine, and all the exemptions you enjoyed as a small cidermaker will disappear.) The duty exemption meant I could charge reasonable prices: I retailed my 500ml bottles at £3 (wholesale they would fetch £22 per case of 12, but I sold very little wholesale); 5L bag-in-boxes retailed at up to £20; and 20L bag-in-boxes, which mostly went to pubs, would fetch £40–£50. (One tradition that was lost in the big reform of liquor licensing in 2003, by the way, was that of farm gate sales. You would today need both a premises licence and a personal licence, but you can sell at farmers' markets and other special occasions using a Temporary Events Notice, or TEN, which you can find out about and apply for at your district council's licensing department.)

Perry

Perry is no more than cider made from pears, and although the word has fallen out of common usage to the extent that many manufacturers of pear-based fruit-flavoured abominations describe it as "pear cider", among afiçionados it is regarded as a far superior beverage and therefore commands a very worthwhile price premium.

One reason why perry fell out of favour was the reputed difficulty of growing the specialised pear varieties that make it. Unlike an apple tree, a standard perry pear tree will grow to park size but will take its time in doing so. Anyone with any curiosity who has visited Herefordshire, Worcestershire, Gloucestershire and Monmouthshire in blossom time (slightly earlier for pears than for apples) cannot have failed to notice the magnificent, towering and usually solitary specimens – some of them more than 300 years old – absolutely smothered in white blossom. Farmers in these parts used to plant a single tree because once grown – and it might take half a century to bear – it would produce quite enough fruit to supply the farm with perry for the year. At harvest time the farmer would simply rope off the tree to keep the livestock at bay and pick up the windfalls. There were always a few perry pear orchards, mainly in Gloucestershire, but the slow growth of the tree was, commercially speaking, a fatal handicap. "He who plants pears," it was said, "plants for his heirs."

But just like apples, pear scions can perfectly easily be grafted on to suitable rootstock, and the Somerset cidermaker Showerings actually planted hundreds of acres of pears to ensure the supply of fruit necessary to supply its Babycham brand (all grubbed up now, sadly). So there's no reason why you shouldn't plant your own Blakeney Red or Yellow Huffcap or Littleton Late Treacle or Berllanderi Red; and if you graft your scions on to quince rootstock the tree will bear within three years and will always remain a manageable size. Visit **www.nationalperrypearcentre.org.uk**.

There is one particular difficulty with perry, however: as with dessert pears, perry pears have to be caught at exactly the right moment. Most varieties have to be picked and milled just before they're perfectly ripe and not allowed to fall, because they very quickly soften after ripening and turn to unpressable goo in the mill – upon which they're no good for anything more than baby food. But if you get it right, fine vintage perry nicely presented in drawn-cork wine bottles is as fine a product as any Chablis and should fetch a similar price.

Cider vinegar

Cider vinegar can be made accidently by allowing air, and with it acetifying bacteria, to come in contact with the cider, or deliberately by setting some of your cider aside (well aside – in a building of its own, preferably), adding vinegar or a 'mother' – ie an acetobacter culture, which you can buy at any home brew shop or online – to start the process off, and leaving the tank or vat open to the air covered with gauze or muslin to keep debris and insects out. It can take a few weeks or a few months for all the alcohol to turn to acetic acid, and the resulting vinegar needs to be matured for a time before bottling. As this is a food substance, a best before date is required on all packaging. The Trading Standards Department at your district council will give you the details.

There is a lucrative market for artisan vinegar, and you can make a profit a third higher than you can on your cider. Its popularity is partly due to claims that it can help lower blood pressure and reduce the risk of heart disease and diabetes: none of this is substantiated, so don't repeat them in your labelling and marketing. Selling unfiltered apple cider vinegar with an active mother as a starter culture might be the makings of a mail order or internet business.

Other opportunities

An orchard is not just a place where fruit grows. It can also be a place for pleasure and leisure, and as we have seen it can be used in many ways. Here are a few more of them.

First, there is the rental fruit tree market. I heard about this some years ago from a friend whose father-in-law had died, and whose family thought renting an apple tree in a small traditional orchard would be an ideal way to remember him. The package included one dedicated visiting weekend in the middle of blossom time and another at harvest, when the relatives were invited to come and collect what fruit they wanted from 'their' tree. All the care and maintenance was carried out by the grower as normal. For the inconvenience of two weekends annually, you might charge £40–£60 (2017 prices) per tree per annum. You will need to keep records of which trees you've rented and maybe place a memorial plaque at the foot of each one and when you get your visitors on site you have the opportunity of selling them your cider, apple juice, jam, eggs or other smallholding products.

Second, late November and December offer the chance of selling mistletoe at the farm gate, on your market stall if you have one, and to local florists, hotels and restaurants (get them to place their orders well in advance!). European mistletoe (*Viscum album*) is a semi-parasitic plant that lives on apple, oak, lime, poplar, hawthorn, maple and willow. Popular opinion will tell you that it will kill your trees and must be avoided at all costs, which isn't true. It's true that mistletoe does indeed have root structures that feed off the host tree, but its green leaves show that it also photosynthises, producing food for itself. If properly managed and not allowed to grow too large for the host, the two can happily co-exist and provide a useful bit of cash in the bleak midwinter. Both male and female shoots (ie berried and unberried) must be pruned, preferably just before the start of the festive season, so the prunings can simply be sold as a crop. Selling mistletoe seeds on the internet in February and March is another niche market. To growing your own mistletoe take at least ten berries off an established plant, carefully remove the seeds from the pulp and keep it in a light dry place until you're ready to infect a host. Ideally this will be the same species as the host you collected the berries from: if the donor was an apple, then infecting another apple with the berries improves their chances of germinating. Choose a high branch open to the sunlight, and preferably a younger branch 2-6cm in diameter. Infect a spot not too near the trunk by pushing five or six of the seeds (either fresh or dried and then moistened) into the bark on the underside of the branch. A little nick in the bark may help introduce the seed, but is not essential. Leave them exposed or tie them on with a little hessian or grafting tape and expect about one in 10 of them to germinate. With luck you'll see green hypocotyls in six to eight weeks. It's a slow-growing plant and can take a few years to get going, so be patient.

Finally, the orchard is a restorative and magical environment ideal for outdoor weddings, festivals and happenings of almost any description. But its possibilities are not limited to the summertime: in fact, it comes into its own in the dead of winter when the dark and short days create a perfect excuse to cheer everyone up with a wassail. This supposedly most ancient of folk customs (first recorded, as it happens, in Fordham, Kent, in 1547, when the farmyards and barns were wassailed as well as the orchards) can be a nice opportunity to sell young apple trees in pots, hot spiced apple juice and of course cider to your guests. Plan (and sell tickets) well ahead, trying to avoid clashes with other wassails in the area. Traditionally wassails are held on one of the many candidates for Twelfth Night (5th, 6th, 16th or 17th January), but who's counting? If you intend to sell cider by the glass or to take away, you'll need a TEN from the district council. A hog roast or even just sausage baps or similar and of course a folk group and the local morris side will create an enjoyable and profitable midwinter event. The first recorded wassail involved the young men of the village dancing round the cattle byres and any other structures that might be haunted or possessed, singing and letting off their muskets. These days the dancers sing the wassail song and toast the trees, whose roots are also liberally doused with cider; and an offering of toast soaked in cider is placed in the branches. In some versions, a (fearless) small child is hoisted into the branches to represent the guardian of the trees, and he or she eats the offering of the toast. A bonfire and torches provide light and atmosphere in the cold and dark; pots and pans are clattered and shotguns are fired to scare off the boggarts. It's all a load of hokum, but it's a load of hokum you can make money from.

Well, there you have just three opportunities for incremental profit and strong word-of-mouth. You will doubtless think of many, many more…

Other opportunities

Case Study

07

Mainstream farming is used to being criticised by environmentalists and wildlife campaigners as overintensive, monocultural and soaked in noxious agrichemicals. And despite government initiatives to promote diversity and good stewardship, these allegations are still widespread and are still, especially in the arable prairies of East Anglia, East Yorkshir and eastern Scotland, borne out by the most obvious of all forms of evidence – i.e., the evidence of your own eyes.

Meanwhile extensive farming and adding value have never been an issue for smallholders. Few smallholdings are big enough to be able to farm intensively or make a living out of a single crop, except some very niche crops: most smallholders need more than one string to their bow if they're to make enough money to live on. Either they produce more than one crop off the same land or they have part-time jobs, often as mechanics, engineers or lecturers or they process their own produce – turning apples into cider, milk into cheese, soft fruit into jam or wine – and live on the value they have added. You will almost certainly find you need to do the same, even if it's only by getting a hay-crop and some hedgefruit or the rent of a summer's keep from your orchard.

But while there is almost no end to the possible sidelines, marginal opportunities and secondary income streams that will present themselves, it's important to remain primarily focused on your core business. You only have so much time, energy and money, so make sure that your lesser ventures don't starve your primary earner of resources. Balance the time and money available to invest in a sideline against the achievable outcome very carefully before settling on a secondary project.

Tourism and leisure

On a smallholding, every building and every scrap of land has to earn its keep. The cost of renovating or altering redundant farm buildings can be high – although less so if you're capable of doing some of the work yourself – but turning unwanted sheds and barns into active space can prove hugely lucrative in the long run, future-proofing the viability of the whole enterprise.

Farm-based holidays require investment whether you provide B&B, log cabins, holiday chalets, yurts, shepherd's huts or caravanning and camping. They also require planning permission, and in the case of camping and caravanning take up land that might well have a more profitable use. But if the pound keeps falling the delights of the British countryside look likely to be even more attractive both to domestic staycationers and to foreign visitors seeking the best possible value for their euro. Of course it's only during the peak periods – school summer and Easter holidays and term-time bank holiday weekends – that tourism earns top dollar. But you can extend the camping season both forwards and back by a fortnight or more by hosting music, food and other festivals; in the off season the same field could be let out for caravan and boat storage. The more weatherproof accommodation can be kept ticking over off-season by price-cuts, except at New Year and Valentine's Day. You could also strike a deal with the owner of a wedding venue to put up entire wedding parties at special rates – more romantic, surely, than a Holiday Inn? You might even have an atmospheric old barn of your own that would make the ideal wedding venue – you need a licence, though, as well as a functions kitchen with lots of staff and adequate parking. In fact you would need some sort of staff presence for almost any tourist activity except B&B – summer jobs for students, perhaps?

Even if you're not in a traditional tourist area you can let surplus outbuildings for a huge range of purposes: there's always a demand for space for self-storage units, yoga and pilates studios, workshops, offices, shops, auctions, even craft breweries and distilleries. Another profitable use for surplus outbuildings – or for brand-new purpose-built runs and housing, for that matter – outside tourist areas is domestic pet boarding. It's a lucrative market, but an expensive one to enter. There are strict criteria regarding dimensions and facilities – proper drainage, electricity, hot and cold water and sneeze barriers are just a few of them – as well as the handling and welfare of your guests. Word of mouth is just as important as official inspections in keeping you up to the mark, so you have to stay on your toes and not let standards slip.

It's a fairly labour-intensive business, too: animals have to be fed, dogs have to be walked, litter has to be changed. You can start charging at £10 a day for a basic cage for a cat or a small-breed dog and £20 or more for a big-breed dog in a luxury kennel. Animal boarding is regulated by the district council: you need to apply for a licence and be inspected under the Animal Boarding Act 1963.

Land itself is more versatile than you might suppose. It doesn't have to be planted or grazed: there's a certain demand for outdoor leisure space such as horse livery, dog agility and obedience training, paintballing, archery, clay pigeon shooting and even allotments. A few years ago, a canny lady who had a smallholding on the outskirts of Falmouth came up with a fantastic way of making money. She'd been cutting the grass in her field for hay for a few hundred pounds a year when she heard that local residents were demanding that the council should provide them with allotments. It was the push she needed. She carved up her hay-field into around 100 plots, both full-size and starter. She put some hard standing down for cars and provided a portable loo. Demand outstripped supply, and after three years she bought a neighbouring field to provide more allotments. The allotments are run organically and irrigated with rainwater collected on site, and a communal hut provides somewhere for the allotment holders to gather and chat. Sometimes it's the simplest ideas that work the best and give the best returns.

Different crops

Any smallholding, particularly as you approach our (admittedly arbitrary) 50-acre upper limit, is going to comprise different sorts of soil suitable for different types of cultivation. And as I said, every scrap of land has to work for its living.

Turf

Perhaps the most basic sort of crop is plain and simple grass; and what country in the world is as good at growing grass as Britain? With our mild climate and frequent and regular rainfall we revel in glorious gardens, golf courses, meadows, football pitches and even green roofs – all products of the turf industry.

In recent years there has been a noticeable increase in new housing developments, with a corresponding increase in demand for turf for gardens, amenity areas, sports facilities and so on. There is a turf type suitable for all levels of wear, moisture and light; even lightweight turf for roofing. Naturally, anyone entering this industry will have to have some training or experience whether as a grower or as a greenkeeper or landscaper. Some private training providers offer suitable courses, and agricultural colleges offer NVQ level 2 courses in sports and amenity turf with Institute of Groundmanship endorsement. Growers have a professional association, the National Turfgrass Council: **www.turfgrass.co.uk**.

Most turf produced in the UK is a mixture of creeping, chewing and red fescues with some rye grass included for robustness and a good root system to give the turf lateral strength when being cut or laid. Maintenance of the turf includes fertilising, mowing and brushing before harvesting in dry weather with a special turf-cutting machine that rolls the turf into uniform lengths. Production follows an 18-month to two-year cycle, and most growers start with a minimum of 20 acres to cover the costs of machinery and labour. Most growers also produce their own compost to replace the soil lost in harvesting.

Turf is a crop like any other crops: it requires seeding, maintenance, harvesting, storage, shipping, marketing and replacement. It is also one of the few crops that is happiest in the cooler areas of the north and west.

Christmas trees and decorative foliage

These are a good option for well-drained soil that's not necessarily suited to mechanical cultivation. It's a good market: the British buy 6-8 million conifers of various kinds at £30–£40 apiece in the countdown to Christmas. That's somewhere between £180,000,000 and £320,000,000 all told; and there's plenty of room in the market for independent growers. Some claim that a single acre can support 4,000 trees; personally I think it's more like 2,700 based on a 4ft square plot per tree; and even with staggered plantings and harvesting at five years plus, that's a gross income of £16,000 with very low labour and chemical input. Having said that, trees aren't entirely input-free: they need sturdy fencing to protect them from rabbits and deer, as well as pruning to ensure a good shape and prevent bolting.

Peak times for labour and sales are naturally from the end of November until the week before Christmas, followed by replanting in spring. Herbicidal sprays in the first two years will allow the trees to establish themselves properly, and judicious use of a selective insecticide such as pirimicarb will deal with sap-sucking aphids while allowing beneficial insects to flourish.

You can steal a march on the garden centres and supermarkets who will be your main rivals partly by undercutting them slightly, but mainly by making the process of choosing and taking away the tree something a bit special. An inviting farm shop selling wreaths and mistletoe as well as trees alongside attractions such as a Santa's Grotto and perhaps a wreath-making workshop (I've done this – it's really easy and very popular) will all attract visitors; and there can be nothing more magical for a child than going up the field with mum and dad and the grower in person, trusty bowsaw in hand, to select that one special tree. Throw in a bit of Santa banter and you can bet they'll be back next year and every year after that!

As for the trees themselves, the old-school Norway Spruce (*Picea abies*) has fallen out of favour and has been largely replaced by species that hold their needles longer and come in different shades. While the most popular tree these days is the Nordmann Fir (*Abies nordmanniana*) with 80 per cent of the market, the Blue Spruce (*Picea pungens glauca*) with its glaucous blue colour is becoming popular, as is the Fraser Fir (*Abies Fraseri*). There are quite a few nurseries where you can buy seedlings, and the return on investment is pretty good if you sell direct to the consumer. For more information visit **www.yctgroup.co.uk**.

Holly and ivy are also good Christmas cash crops, as is mistletoe.

I've included more detailed information about mistletoe in the chapter on orchards, so we will touch only on the holly and the ivy here.

Holly is a native British species that has many varieties. Only the female plant produces berries, but you will of course need a male plant hanging around in the background somewhere if you're going to get a berry crop, so plant both sexes. It's happy in most soils and situations and only really dislikes very wet soil. You can propagate from hardwood cuttings or indeed graft chosen varieties on to native Ilex aquifolium rootstocks. When choosing varieties you need to look at colour AND sex. This can be quite confusing: Silver Queen with its glossy dark green silver-edged spiky leaves is actually male and therefore bears no berries but the spike-free Golden King with its lovely red berries is, of course, female. Get both, together with a female native dark-leaved *Ilex aquifolium*.

For ivy, Hedera helix Goldheart is an excellent foliage plant and will produce long streams of variegated green and gold leaves. Silver Queen (a different Silver Queen!) has variegated green and white leaves.

Christmas wreaths can be made quickly and quite simply with a ring of willow (make these up in the spring) with holly and ivy entwined round it finished off with a red or gold bow and maybe a bauble or two. They'll fetch £4–£8, so there isn't a huge profit in them, but they're incremental to the tree sale, and you can also sell the decorative greenery to florists, pubs, hotels and restaurants.

Lavender

The familiar blue-to-mauve aromatic shrub and its cousin lavandin, named for their age-old use in scenting fresh laundry, are high-value crops for the cosmetics industry, with dried flowers and oil being the two saleable products. Growing them is becoming increasingly popular, especially among cereal farmers seeking to diversify.

Fields of lavender have one great advantage over most other crops: they are stunningly beautiful. This makes them an attraction in their own right, on the back of which you can build a retail business specialising in the many manifestations of the lavender itself as well as all the other goods you (and perhaps your neighbours) produce.

Products such as lavender and lavandulin bags and pillows are eternally popular; and lavender can be combined with hops or wheat for microwaveable muscle soothers. Offering plants for sale is an obvious option, and a multitude of culinary uses include infusion in dry sugar or syrup to flavour cream, cake filling, butter, icing, chocolate, ice cream, sorbet, meringues, vodka – almost anything, really. Traditional herbs de Provence include lavender as part of the mix. It can be used with honey as a glaze for roast duck or with chocolate for venison. And try infusing it with apricots to make a heady Mediterranean jam!

It's a great convenience that lavender is in full bloom at the height of summer, evoking Provence just when there are most likely to be tourists about. Open days with tours and picnics are therefore more or less guaranteed to generate a good income, although given the unpredictability of the British summer the need for staff, parking, toilet facilities and so on do represent quite a risk. Allowing the fields to be used for commercial photography and filming is a nice little bonus, too.

Lavender requires sunny, warm, well-drained, light, alkaline soil, preferably with chalk or lime content and is frequently planted through polythene or weed-mat as you can't use herbicidal sprays on crops destined for culinary, pharmaceutical or cosmetic use. (If you want the rows of lavender nearest the shop and café to look pretty, lay a mulch of bright white sand and / or crushed oyster shell between the rows.) Harvesting stands in for pruning, so there's no double-handling. The plants will last for eight or nine years before they have to be replaced.

Different varieties suit different purposes. *Lavandula angustifolia* produces a high-quality essential oil suitable for perfumes and *L. Intermedia* (technically a lavandin, not a lavender) produces around 50 per cent more essential oil but of a lesser quality, more suited to soap and massage, aromatherapy and pot pourri oil. Both have antiseptic qualities. To produce dry lavender, the flowers are harvested when the first couple of buds on the stem have opened. Long-stemmed lavender makes perfect decorative bunches, while shorter stems are ideal for drying for pot pourri and pillows.

The oil is extracted by steam distillation: the tops are seethed in boiling water or live steam until it evaporates and is carried off to condense in a tank, where the lighter oil sits on top of the water and can then be drawn off for packaging. A realistic yield from varieties such as Mailette and Folgate of around 40 litres an acre can fetch upwards of £50 a litre; Grosso lavandin can yield double that amount but at only £20 a litre.

At time of writing the crop also qualifies for single farm payments, although Brexit might well change all that!

Cut flowers and decorative foliage

Traditional favourites such as chrysanthemums and carnations have taken a beating since the 1960s, and there are only a few producers left. Daffs and narcissi are still popular, though, both as bulbs and cut flowers. The south west, the Scillies and the Channel Islands where mild winters and early springs promote early growth and satisfy demand for spring flowers have always been the main centres of production, but Bedfordshire and other traditional centres of market gardening are important centres too, where the budding horticultural entrepreneur will still find good growing conditions, networks of suppliers and access to markets.

The British cut-flower market is worth £2.2bn retail, of which 90 per cent is channelled through supermarkets; but there's increasing demand in the hospitality and wedding trades as well a growing corporate market for fresh displays in prestige offices and at promotional events. This coupled with climate change has seen British growers challenge the dominance of importers, and the acreage devoted to flowers has expanded by more than 30 per cent in the past five years. Unfortunately the prices are dictated by multiple retailers who can of course sell flowers very cheaply. But restaurants, hotels and corporate hospitality buyers are demanding (and getting) an ever-wider variety of ornamentals including hebes, eucalyptus, ivies and winter-flowering specials such as witch hazel, corkscrew hazel, and phormium leaves. Relatively new entrants into the cut flower market include sunflowers, lilacs, hydrangeas, sweet peas and British wild flowers such as sweet rocket and foxgloves; and domestic growers are exploiting the fact that British flowers retain their scent better than forced foreign imports to make the local choice more attractive and worth that little bit extra.

Most cut-flower producers are big, heavily-capitalised enterprises with large overheads in chemical input and mainly seasonal labour. But I know smallholders in Cornwall who have made good returns from growing cut flowers and greenery on less than an acre, requiring no more than a polytunnel for the more delicate blooms, applying no chemicals and hiring no pickers. By using harvested rainwater, biomass boilers and solar panels, production costs can be slashed and the normal growing season can be extended.

Willow

Traditional willow, rattan and hazel baskets have become popular decorative items both in the home and in the retail and hospitality trades. Working creatively with willow has expanded into landscape design, furniture making and living sculpture. Our heightened awareness of sustainability has even led us to choose willow coffins as a way to make an emphatic final statement.

Willows are our fastest-growing and highest-yielding tree or shrub and are particularly suited to cool and damp conditions. They are also very versatile. The long, strong, slender, flexible twigs or withies are plaited and then twisted round the harder, thicker sticks to make trugs and baskets of all shapes and sizes, elegant outdoor or indoor furniture, hurdles, screens, blinds and 101 other things. They come in many colours, to fire your imagination yet further. The setts or cuttings can also be sold to gardeners, as can bundles of sticks and withies for hobby basketmakers. Another market is giving talks or exhibitions of your work and offering courses on basketry or making Christmas wreaths or garden sculptures. Many Christmas fairs, country craft markets and agricultural shows even employ willow weavers to run drop-in events where children and parents can make a small basic item to take home.

Take advantage of the long, dark evenings of winter and early spring to build up a stock of top-quality items for sale at shows, craft fairs or online. Costs are minimal but weaving is a laborious process (until you get used to it) and retail prices aren't high, so only direct sales of premium products will make you a worthwhile profit.

Willow rods grow from a stump-like stool that take about three years from planting to harvesting. The beds are harvested in winter when bare, and each stool can produce up to 30 rods of around eight feet long. They are easy to grow and require little input.

Willow and other similar coppice have more uses than producing baskets and rods. Short rotation coppicing is a quick and efficient method of producing wood for fuel, either as whole logs (taking around five years) or woodchip (around three) for biomass boilers. Good varieties to grow include *Salix viminalis gigantea* or *S. viminalis Bowles Hybrid*. A five-year short rotation coppice planted 1m apart in 1.5m spaced rows will produce around six tonnes of firewood an acre every five years. Take precautions to keep grazers out, as all animals like willow. You will also need storage space to dry the wood.

Pharmaceutical crops

You may not know it, but pharmaceutical crops are quite widely grown around Britain, often on quite small plots and in total secrecy under the guardianship of private companies retained by the government. Often the reward for a contract with one of these companies is not great; but then the contractor usually carries out the harvest on security grounds. Opportunities in this field may be rare, but they are still worth enquiring after.

The opium poppy, *Papaver somniferum*, has been a legal crop in the UK since 2002, when there was a worldwide shortage of opiates; and today there are fields of rather mysterious mauve and lilac flowers dotted around Oxfordshire, Northamptonshire, Dorset and Lincolnshire where the light soils suit their cultivation. The contractor for opium poppies is Scottish drug company Macfarlan Smith, which licences growers on around 7,000 acres around the country. The yield should be around 15kg a hectare, which is worth £1,000 to the farmer. Not bad for a spring-sown break-crop!

Case study

Coddington Christmas Trees, Ledbury, Herefordshire

After studying agriculture, Colin Palmer spent many years in the agrochemical sector including 20 years at Shell Chemicals where he was responsible for pesticide training and product development. In 1974 he bought a three-acre smallholding and set up Coddington Christmas Trees and Rural Services, both selling Christmas trees and consulting and training in weed, pest and disease control.

The plot, set in woodland at an altitude of 160m, included a derelict 1830s house with no vehicle access of its own, which was being used as animal housing and was at risk of being demolished. After a planning wrangle Colin was able to renovate it and has since replaced its old timber barn with a modern 200m^2 steel building suitable for his agricultural and forestry business.

Colin learnt about growing Christmas trees the hard way through trial and error, but he's always been open about his failures as well as his triumphs: for instance, his first crop of Norway Spruce was devastated by green spruce aphid, which considering his background... That apart, his background has proved invaluable and the business is thriving, providing a range of different varieties for the local market. The sales window is a mere three–four weeks in the run-up to Christmas, but Colin is busy throughout the year with planting, pruning and maintenance as well as running his consultancy. He is always being asked if Christmas trees make a good crop for small plots; his 2016 book *Christmas Trees – A Grower's Guide* aims to give the answer.

With a regular planting scheme taking into account that the average tree takes eight years to mature, and noting that trees need to be spaced around 1.5m apart, it's possible to stagger-plant around 1,500 trees an acre, giving an annual crop of some 187 trees at £30 or more each or a turnover of £5,610 per acre. Costs include labour, seedlings (currently less than £1), pesticides and netting. Necessary skills include basic horticulture, pruning, spraying and knowing what makes a good tree. This latter comes with experience, but a good tree will be between a metre and two metres tall, with a classic taper and 9–15 inch gaps between the branch tiers. Colder winters produce better-shaped trees, as mild winters encourage the leader shoot to grow too quickly.

But, says Colin, strong marketing skills are the most important of all. Produce an attractive marketing campaign with the best photographs you can get: in this market, visuals are the determining factor. It also creates a point of difference if you offer to take the trees back to recycle as compost, mulch or biomass fuel that you can sell to offset your costs. Investigate other seasonal crops too, such as mistletoe, seasonal greenery and Christmas wreaths, and accessories such as Christmas tree stands. Visit **www.treesplease.co/uk/wp-content/uploads/2015/10/Trees-Please-Christmas-Tree-Advice.pdf**.

Taxus baccata (English yew, Irish yew and Golden yew) is infamous because all parts of the tree are poisonous. However the needles also produce the taxanes used to treat cancer and are harvested between May and October. Friendship Estates in Doncaster collects and pays for annual clippings. For details, contact **www.friendshipestates.co.uk**.

Contracting, seasonal, and relief work

Many smallholders make extra cash by hiring out their services to other smallholders or even mainstream farmers either at busy times, or as specialists in one field or another or as sickness / holiday cover. If you find that there are times when you have some spare capacity, this is a good way of earning some ready money and is also, crucially, the foundation of a business and social network in a sphere of operations where isolation can be a terrible affliction.

Agricultural services

At harvest time or whenever staff and machinery are stretched, relying on contractors is cheaper than hiring or buying. Traditional seasonal jobs such as cutting and topping paddocks, ploughing, hedging and ditching, hay cutting and baling, and fencing and timber work are also often contracted out, and then there are one-off jobs such as removing dung heaps and muck-spreading.

Although the work may be unpredictable, agricultural contracting might suit a semi-retired farmworker or a smallholder with other income streams as well. And smallholders themselves often use contractors for smaller jobs that don't justify the expense of buying specialised equipment. Hourly rates start at around £25 depending on the job and the machinery required: visit **www.naac.co.uk**.

Lambing

The traditional lambing season has been extended thanks to new breeding techniques, and help with lambing, especially at night, is now in demand from late November until mid-April. For a lambing nightshift of 8–12 hours you could earn £10–£15 per hour.

Mobile shearing

With the right skills you can also offer a mobile shearing service for other smallholders: most large sheep farms hire the travelling shearers from Australia and New Zealand who will only cater for flocks of 200 upwards. The smallholder with 10 sheep that need shearing often struggles to find a shearer but the job has to be done for the sheep's sake, and it's a great opportunity for someone fit and healthy and with a little experience. The rate at time of writing is about £2 a beast, but you should agree a minimum charge plus fuel to make it worth your while.

Relief milking

As a part-time service offered as holiday or sickness cover, a normal four-hour milking shift should pay £40–£50. You will need enough experience to be trusted to work on your own.

Milk recording

This requires meticulous accuracy in taking samples from dairy cows. You need your own transport and will be paid a set rate with travel expenses that works out to about £12 per hour. Most milk recorders work on a self-employed basis for a company called National Milk Records that collects information on individual animals' milk yield and quality and fertility. The recorder visits monthly to take samples. and farm visits last a couple of hours each.

Drystone walling

Stone walls built without mortar or cement are common in regions where stone is plentiful but wood is scarce all over Great Britain and Ireland, with different local styles evolved from the types of stone available. In Cornwall, for instance, the wall is hollow and filled with soil and small stones known as shillet, topped with a living hedge. Drystone walls make durable and attractive boundary markers, field enclosures and animal shelters. In the dim distant past the technique was also used to build sheds, barns, pigsties, even whole cottages, many of which can still be seen in rocky upland country. More recently we've seen quite a large revival of interest in drystone walling as a more enduring, cost-effective and sustainable method of enclosure than fencing.

Any waller will warn you that you need a special quality to succeed in the craft: an appetite for long hours of hard graft on your own in all weathers in the middle of nowhere. You also need experience and training: you may have started out repairing sections on your own holding, progressed to helping out your neighbours and then decided to train properly in the art. There are training providers all over the country such as **www.wallsforthefuture.co.uk** and through Lantra, **www.lantra.co.uk**. Also check the Drystone Wallers Association, **www.dsw.org.uk**.

The work itself is slow and painstaking and demands intense concentration to ensure that whatever the job on hand, whether new build or repair, it's done thoroughly, safely and with an eye for detail that will produce a wall both sturdy and in keeping with the local style. It's got to be right, too: you don't want to be coming back!

A proficient drystone waller should be able to complete 3–4m^3 a day, depending on the weather, so fix your daily rate accordingly. (Only the National Trust and English Heritage are likely to pay by the hour.) A typical charge would be £100 per m^3 if you're supplying the stone, £60 if you're not. But be warned: you will face competition from semi-professionals – landscape gardeners and the like – who will undercut you ruthlessly, especially on the smaller patching-up jobs. Part of your pitch should therefore be that the prospective client has two choices: pay the cheapjack rate now and your rate in a year or two's time, or pay your rate now and nothing more for a century!

Those who can... teach

08

Case Study

As a training co-ordinator for the Rural Business School in Cornwall, I found that among the students were a number of working farmers and growers who wanted to expand their knowledge of a wide range of subjects both at certificated and uncertificated levels. You need formal qualifications for some areas of work on the holding, but by no means for all; some people, though, just feel happier having a certificate even if they don't really need one. We all have to accept that we can't learn everything, but to master the skills we lack we may have to pay someone else for their expertise. And who better to pay than someone who's done it all not once but every day – maybe someone like you?

The right stuff

There's a steady demand for courses in horticulture, agriculture, animal husbandry and other rural skills, many of which are taught formally in classrooms in community colleges and other similar venues, but many of which can't be taught in conventional settings. After all, you can't really demonstrate how to kill and dress a chicken for the table in a classroom! You might want to sign up to teach a part-time or evening course at a local college, but if you have the appropriate facilities – parking, toilets and somewhere that will stand in for a classroom – and a subject that people are eager to learn, then it might be worth considering whether you have the qualities you need to make extra money by passing your knowledge on to others.

Teaching is a flexible skill. It may be one-to-one or 1/100; it can be a lecture, a practical demonstration, a day course or a set of classes over a few weeks. Each situation is as different and as unique as each learner. The snide old saying "those that can – do, and those that can't – teach" couldn't be further from the truth: teaching is a skill that most doers simply don't possess. A good teacher will engage their learners with interesting and informative lessons, and be able to measure the learners' knowledge both at the start and at the end of a lesson – that doesn't just happen by chance. A lot of work goes into lesson planning, with a variety of teaching styles included because we all learn differently. Some of us like to read to learn, others to watch a video or demonstration; others prefer to act out or practice a task physically. Some of us learn better on our own and others in groups, and a good lesson will try to cover a subject in a variety of activities and tasks.

As a result teaching is a great responsibility. It is tiring and demanding, and if you mess up then your failure is horribly visible. We can all have off days, but if teaching is your livelihood then negative feedback – or worse still negative feedback on social media – will seriously affect your ability to attract new students. Being professional and businesslike has to be the order of the day from putting a course together and making sure your professional paperwork is in order and valid to delivering appropriate teaching.

Good teachers need more than subject knowledge, suitable premises and time. Effective communication and interpersonal skills are essential. If you don't like people then you're going to struggle, and both you and your learners are going to have a less than perfect experience. You need the confidence to remain calm and professional even when things don't go to plan. Organisational skills are of critical importance – it's up to you to ensure your learners know where, when and what they are doing; you need to plan what you intend to deliver and have any activities, handouts, demonstrations, props etc. in place. Examine what relevant prior experience you have – a career in the services or in a supervisory or management role, for example, or even in bringing up a family – that have given you the qualities that enable you to teach, tutor or coach.

Organisational and managerial skills, though, should be deployed to enhance rather than overshadow that all-important virtue of flexibility. Not all learners learn at the same pace or to the same level. This can lead to conflict; which you as the teacher, need to control and diffuse. You need to motivate and reward *all* your learners and be able to empathise and encourage when they just don't get it despite your best efforts. Also, you need to remember that unlike school students adult learners often have complicated lives and may have issues with childcare, finance or health.

Adult learning

Most of the teaching within agriculture, horticulture and rural skills is aimed at adults. While there is demand among younger people, informal providers such as a farm-based instructor will have problems getting the appropriate insurance. As a result it tends to be schools that offer learning opportunities within the national curriculum's environmental and land-based science syllabus. Other learning providers for youngsters include Young Farmers Clubs **www.nfyfc.org.uk**, which also run Train the Trainer events for anyone who would like to try their hand at teaching.

Your learners will therefore be adults who are well-motivated and have high expectations of you. However, they are all individuals with different levels of experience, different levels of education and different amounts of time they can devote to learning. By clearly defining the level you are offering, together with information such as start and finishing times, how many sessions the course includes and whether there will be any homework, you will help your aspiring learners to choose the most suitable course for their needs and circumstances. Here, as an example, are the different courses and syllabuses you might offer to cover a single subject, in this case beekeeping.

- An introductory "beekeeping experience" might be a short taster suitable for all levels of interest, perhaps combining a visit to an apiary with some discussion of what beekeeping is all about. The session would last two to three hours, and there would be no handouts or notes.
- A beginners' course would possibly last six hours, with a short practical session with the bees and longer spent in a classroom with handouts and possibly a slideshow or Powerpoint presentation.
- An intermediate beekeeping course might consist of eight two-hour sessions with notes, homework, some practical experience and some kind of test at the end, either with or without certification.

For learners with absolutely no experience, the introductory session provides them with basic information about what is entailed and a practical session without committing either time or expense. If it transpires that the learner is terrified of bees or is claustrophobic in the beesuit then nothing is lost. A short, cheap, no-strings intro of this sort is very popular with many learners and represents an income stream even if many of the candidates decide not to progress. The level of expertise required by the tutor can vary.

Those who progress to the beginners' course should expect to learn enough to take up beekeeping as a hobby, and the intermediate course to turn a hobby into a business. The tutor or teacher in this case had better know their stuff and should also be prepared to tailor their teaching to the learners' needs.

Teaching on the farm

What can you teach on your own premises depends not only on your knowledge and experience but also on the facilities you have. Our smallholding had an orchard; we kept bees and chickens; we reared bottle-fed lambs; and we made cider. John had a working forge and two welding bays. That meant we could teach beekeeping, chicken keeping, practical lambing, orchard skills, cidermaking, blacksmithing and welding.

Your own ambitions as a teacher will be determined to some extent, as ours were, by the limitations of your holding; but there are other factors to take into account too. Researching what subjects and courses are already on offer in the area is the obvious first step. John was the only private welding instructor for over 100 miles, so he had quite a few learners over the years and was also a tutor at the Rural Business School. His one-day beginners' workshops in blacksmithing proved very popular as Christmas and birthday gifts – a handy marketing tip for you there! On the other hand the growing popularity of community apple groups offering very cheap tuition limited the number of pruning workshops I could fill – although I could run two cidermaking workshops in October because there was no other provision in the area. All in all we did very well out of seasonal courses and made some great friends over the years.

Hosting courses on your smallholding is less formal and undeniably more fun than holding evening classes in the more formal surroundings of your local community college. But it is no less demanding of your teaching skills and of the diligent preparation of course materials. If you are giving a talk or a presentation, then you have little option but to have a stationary audience and not much interaction, so I always liked to create opportunities to ask the students a question or two as we went along. This would let me know how well they were following and reassure me that they hadn't fallen asleep!

Sometimes at the end of a talk I would produce samples, which always went down well when I was teaching cidermaking. A variety of suitable props and tasks that the students actually had to carry out had great illustrative value. The climax of my one-day chicken-keeping course, for example, was humane dispatch. I offered this both in council-run leisure classes and at the Rural Business School and was well aware that not every prospective chickenkeeper was keen on the idea of dispatch at all; but I thought animal owners needed to take responsibility for their livestock and be able to put them down in the event of injury, illness or predator attack. As the day edged towards the end, the atmosphere would become very serious and one or two learners would often ask to be excused. Then I'd reveal my secret prop – a rubber chicken bought at a pet shop. Not only did it lighten the atmosphere, but I actually used it to demonstrate humane slaughter without making anyone sick.

Qualifications

As we have seen, I could teach a fairly wide range of subjects on the basis of experience alone but that doesn't mean I had no letters after my name at all. When I started teaching horticulture for Cornwall Adult Education I had one Level 3 Award in horticulture and another in education and training, which was enough to allow me to start formal teaching in the Lifelong Learning Sector. I also began work as a part-time tutor for the Rural Business School, which offered short courses or training in rural skills, agriculture and horticulture. Working for both organisations made me a more confident and competent teacher and provided me with a classroom or workshop and, most importantly, insurance. If you are thinking of teaching this is a career path I would recommend before you begin to search for insurance to teach from your own premises. (You will also need to complete a Disclosure Form to get a criminal record check.) Another benefit of working for a college or institution is that you get instruction in other procedures such as writing risk assessments and lesson plans and making your own teaching materials and Powerpoint presentations. You can also sit in on classes and watch other teachers as well as benefiting from in-house training such as Continued Professional Development. All this will be invaluable when you are preparing your own courses or workshops.

Talks

Community teaching is another avenue you may wish to explore. Organisations such as Women's Institutes and gardening clubs customarily hire evening speakers: an hour-long talk that may include a Powerpoint presentation or slide show and appropriate props should net you around £50 and is also good practice. An hour is a long time to keep the attention of an audience, so you need to break it up for the sake of variety. I put together a presentation on cidermaking for local gardening groups, which started with a comparative tasting of dessert and cider apples, followed by a 20-minute slide show and concluding with a tasting. This broke the presentation down into neat sections – an appetiser, a main and a dessert, if you will – that held the audience's attention, with a final Q&A session standing in for coffee and cigars. The cost to me was a few apples and a couple of bottles of cider. The resources for the talk were all kept in a file, and I must have made at least £1,000 from taking it down off its shelf every autumn. If you fancy doing talks, you need to contact your groups at least a year in advance and tell them what you do and what you require, i.e. a socket, a table and a white wall.

Risk assessments

Risk assessments are mandatory if you're preparing to teach outside a classroom or engage in an activity that requires equipment or tools.

Classroom-based learning is already assessed by the college or council to cover such potential risks as projectors, cables, computer screens and so forth, so as a college tutor all you need to do is survey your classroom for trip hazards such as cables and tell your learners to keep their bags under the table for the same reason.

Outside the classroom it's a different matter. A risk assessment for practical lambing, for example, will include protective clothing, hand-washing facilities, separate areas for food and drink, animal handling, dealing with and disposal of animal fluids and waste, first aid provision, emergency telephone provision, tutor assistance, lighting, personal hygiene information, assessment of slips and trips and size of group. And if you think that covers it all, a risk assessment for a group that includes learners with physical or mental impairment is going to be more detailed still, and you may find you need a learning support assistant who will require details of the learner's particular needs.

The more complex or dangerous the course or activity might be, the more detailed the risk assessment. That doesn't mean the activity can't go ahead, it just means that you should be able to show you were prepared to deal with whatever might crop up. There are many sample risk assessments on the internet and at schools and colleges for you to tailor to your specific needs; basically, this is the ground they all cover:

- Identifing hazards (i.e. anything that may cause harm whether physical, mental, chemical or biological)
- Deciding who may be harmed and how (i.e. teacher/ learners or all, especially noting young, disabled or vulnerable)
- Assessing the risks (how likely/how severe) and taking preventative action
- Recording all the above
- Reviewing at least every six months or when equipment is introduced or removed or conditions change.

Opposite is the risk assessment I drew up for a course I conducted at my smallholding.

Risk Assessment reference no: AG0033
Location: Spotty Dog Cider, Wadebridge, PL27 6EL
Activity: Apple juicing

Hazard or harm	Who is at risk?	How are risks currently controlled?	Are additional control measured needed?
Weight of equipment/ apples – risk of strain through lifting. Risk of equipment falling over on to operators.	Learners, tutor.	Lift only as instructed and with care, using help if necessary. Ensure mill & press are set up correctly and on a level surface.	No
Hygiene – contamination risk from machinery.	End consumer of juice products.	Wash all equipment prior to use, sterilising if necessary. Ensure press operator takes precautions to avoid contamination of pulp with dirty hands.	No
Contamination risk from dirty/rotten fruit.	End consumers, learners, tutor.	Remove all rotten fruit, foreign bodies. Wash all fruit in regularly changed clean water with Campden tablets added to sterilise. Remind users that juice is NOT pasteurised and therefore must be refrigerated/used within four days.	No
Contamination risk from containers.	End consumer	All new and reused containers must be clean and if possible sterilised.	No
Contamination risk from dirty clothing/ footwear/hands of operators.	End consumer	Ensure participants are aware and follow recommendations for clean clothing, footwear and wash hands regularly throughout event. Continual supervision of press while in operation.	No
Mill use risks – electric shock.	Learners, tutor.	Ensure mill is PAT tested, use RCD device, do not use with wet hands	No

Hazard or harm	Who is at risk?	How are risks currently controlled?	Are additional control measured needed?
Trip hazard, mill blade injury to hands.	Learners, tutor.	Arrange cables safely to avoid trip hazard, ensure all users are reminded of risk. Ensure hopper is bolted to mill before use. Do not overload. Disconnect from electricity before removing hopper if it jams. Ensure learners are fully trained and supervised in mill operation.	No
Press use injury – press arm may fall when cheeses are being loaded.	Learners, tutor.	Ensure press arm is firmly held while press is being loaded. Ensure press is clear before lowering press arm.	No

Action required to Reduce Risk
By Whom
See above actions proposed to reduce risk
Tutor
Person carrying out Risk Assessment
Lorraine Turnbull, Tutor
Date of Assessment
19/04/2016
Review date
19/10/2016
Risk Assessment level: Negligible/Slight.

Other requirements

If you host outdoor courses at your own premises you will need public liability insurance, adequate toilet facilities, and a designated first aider with first aid box and accident book. Indoors you will also need a fire safety plan with exits marked, working fire extinguishers, adequate heating and ventilation, possibly a classroom with tables and chairs, a projector and screen and probably a laptop. Workshop teaching such as the welding and blacksmithing courses that John taught requires much more technical and safety rules and storage. You don't need a food hygiene certificate to offer your learners tea and biscuits or even a full meal, but as you are probably already a registered food business you are subject to environmental health inspections.

Disabled access

Making proper provision for learners with disabilities is a must but is not without its challenges. The public institutions I used to work for were asked from time to time to enrol learners with disabilities. Naturally they wanted to be seen to be providing learning for all, and indeed under the 2010 Equality Act they have a duty to do so. But in practice reconciling the physical requirements of the subject and the additional support that would be necessary to meet the needs of students with disabilities with the learning experience of the other students sometimes proved impossible.

I was once asked to include a wheelchair user on a farm-based practical lambing workshop. To accommodate this learner alongside the others would have been very difficult: we would have had to cut the group size to allow everyone their hands-on experience, and also to have had at least one learning support assistant in attendance that meant the course would have run at a loss. I would have had to write a bespoke risk assessment to cover additional hazards including contamination of the wheelchair, access, safe handling and lifting; but it was the prospect of trying to manoeuvre both a ewe in labour and the wheelchair to allow full participation that proved to be the insurmountable hurdle. Sadly it was decided that we couldn't accommodate this particular learner's needs.

I did, however, include a registered blind person on one of my winter pruning courses at Spotty Dog Cider. She came with her husband as her learning support assistant, and I produced handouts in enormous print. In the first half of the course, which was

Case study

Jekka's Herb Farm, Alveston, Gloucestershire

www.jekkas.com

Jekka McVicar started growing herbs as a hobby in 1984 when fresh herbs were really only available in garden centres. Eventually she started to supply local shops before landing a contract with Fortnum & Mason, and started to expand the range she was growing.

A few years later the family moved to its present home, a derelict blacksmith's cottage on two acres, building the business while renovating the house. The business now has four acres and grows 650 varieties, all organic, in plastic polytunnels, glasshouses and agricultural storage sheds with automated watering systems. Jekka recommends planting in full sun and uses soil-based plant compost – that she makes on site – both for propagating and growing her herbs as it retains moisture better than potting compost.

Jekka has no formal horticultural training but has developed her skills from her love of plants and cooking. She has won more than 60 Royal Horticultural Society gold medals for herb displays and in 2012 was awarded the Garden Media Guild Lifetime Achievement Award for services to horticulture, design, education and communication, and excellence in the field of organic herb growing. Celebrity chefs habitually order her produce, and she has designed gardens for Jamie Oliver and Raymond Blanc. She is also developing a range of herbal teas.

It hasn't all been unalloyed success. For ten years she ran a mail-order business but finally had to pull the plug because plants were so often damaged in transit. She still sells books and seeds in her online shop, but plants have to be bought from the farm on the twice-monthly open days or ordered in advance and collected. The farm is between Bristol and Gloucester, with good transport links and a large population within easy reach, so the open days are well-attended.

As with so many passionate people, passing on her knowledge was always important to Jekka. "What I really wanted to do was teach practical horticulture," she says. In 2013 the opportunity to fulfil her ambition finally arrived when she opened her 'Herbetum', a custom-built resource centre with more than 300 varieties of herb on display. She is now able to move the business in a different direction, with more emphasis on education. She now offers masterclasses at £185 a head to introduce gardeners to herbs and upgrade their general horticultural acumen, and they sell out months in advance.

"There are so many skills needed in horticulture," she says, protesting that while there are plenty of courses in gardening agricultural colleges are lagging behind in the teaching of commercial horticulture. "If you work in horticulture there is always something else to know," she adds. "You never, ever stop learning. How to prune a plant, when to prune, knowledge about soil, all these things; and passing on that practical knowledge is really important."

classroom-based, all went well. But in the outdoors practical I had to constantly remind her husband to follow the requirements in the risk assessment regarding hand tool use, awareness of other users and of the hazard presented by bare twigs and branches at eye height, especially in poor light. The day was a success, and the student wanted to attend more courses including a cidermaking workshop. But because of the noise, the fast-moving and extremely dangerous equipment and the additional cost of a professional learning support assistant (the support provided by her husband wasn't really adequate) I reluctantly had to turn her down on safety grounds.

Structuring classes and courses

Learners are happiest in a relaxed and friendly atmosphere. In an old-style classroom you can help create it by arranging the seats in a circle rather than rows, remembering to put visual aids such as flipcharts, whiteboard and screen where everyone can see them. A friendly greeting and a cup of tea or coffee is a good start, and an update on house rules such as the smoking policy, breaks, location of toilets and so on will help put everyone at their ease.

Before you launch into the lesson proper find out how much your learners already know via a general discussion. This breaks the ice as well as helping you weigh up the new intake. For instance, if I were running a pruning workshop I'd ask how many people had their own apple trees and how many had done any pruning at all. The discussion would usually progress from there as the learners start to contribute. I would then write two or three aims or objectives (basically a summary of what I intend to cover) on a whiteboard that I would revisit at the end of the day.

Anyone planning to deliver a speech or a lesson or practical demonstration will need some sort of notes, whether prompt-cards or a full-blown lesson plan. For one-day workshops I usually wrote a single side of A4, but for a course of six lessons I would produce a lesson plan for each day and a session plan to cover the whole course. This allowed me a bit of latitude to alter and move the lessons around according to factors such as the weather or the group's progress. A lesson plan is a flexible document and should be used as such.

If after the end of a lesson you felt that a particular activity or part of the lesson didn't get the results you hoped for, then examine it and amend the plan. Did you run out of time? Was the activity too easy or too complex? Make changes and review. It might take a couple of lessons to iron out timings of activities. Sometimes if things are going wrong having another teacher sit in and see through fresh eyes can identify and resolve the problem.

Running through what you plan to cover in a lesson or workshop is very important and becomes easier as you gain experience. Taking the example of the one-day apple juicing workshop as detailed in the risk assessment, you might think that it only needs an afternoon. But when you start to break down the activities and combine theoretical classroom-based learning with the practical activity, you can see that it really needs a full six-hour workshop. You also need to factor in tea, lunch or comfort breaks, which can become more of a problem when teaching outdoor subjects in winter, such as tree pruning or lambing; and of course you have to leave enough time for a Q&A session.

Breaking a lesson down into short periods allows you to divide it with breaks or to change your delivery style. It's a long day if you have a three-hour slot in the morning for a Powerpoint presentation. I liked to start with a gentle introduction, possibly accompanied by tea and biscuits, so a relevant film clip (YouTube offers a wealth of material or you can prepare your own) or a short slot with props may be a good way to break the ice. I also like to follow an intensive session where perhaps I've introduced some maths or scientific vocabulary with something completely different.

Adult learners are sometimes resistant to working in pairs or groups, so to get round it I have occasionally tried splitting the group in two. This worked well if I introduced an element of competition, such as having a mini-quiz at the end of the day. By then learners had started to get to know each other and ware more open to working together. Praise played a vital part here: some learners have difficulty socialising with complete strangers: they might feel anxious that they don't know as much as everybody else, or they might just be shy about contributing in a group. Lots of encouragement and praise will help them to join in.

Allowing time for students to share their thoughts with you allows you to assess their progress, revisit things they didn't understand or felt difficult or explain things in a different way. Remind hesitant learners of the progress they've made since arriving that morning. If it's a one-day workshop, offer information on how they can progress further learning be it via YouTube, books or courses available elsewhere.

I've detailed a basic lesson plan opposite, but you can simplify or add to it as best suits your requirements.

Session Plan – Juicing workshop
Tutor – Lorraine Turnbull
10am –1pm, 1.30pm–4.30pm
Spotty Dog Cider

AIMS: To enable learners to confidently begin to make apple juice and craft cider
OBJECTIVES: All learners will operate juicing machinery safely, most learners will identify dessert, culinary & cider apples, all learners will be able to list necessary equipment and process.

TIMING	CONTENT	LEARNER ACTIVITIES	RESOURCES	ASSESSMENT
10.00–10.30	Introduction & induction, review of aims & objectives of workshop.	Identify support from tutor. Recognise own personal objectives, ascertain own prior experience in subject.	Register, risk assessment, course information sheet, initial assessment discussion	Discussion to identify level of learning – self-assessment by learner, assessment by tutor.
10.30–11.15	Apple varieties & characteristics – what they impart to juice & cider.	Identify different types of apple – dessert, culinary & cider.	PP presentation. Samples of apples for tasting.	Group discussion followed by individual Q&A on tastes.

TIMING	CONTENT	LEARNER ACTIVITIES	RESOURCES	ASSESSMENT
11.15–12.00	Equipment & process.	Examine equipment, follow flowchart, group discussion. Learn food safety information	Pressing rack, pulper, flowchart, pH paper, hydrometer Handout. Patchulin handout.	Contribute to group discussion, individual Q&A to identify equipment and order of flowchart.
1200–13.00	Making cider – fermentation & maturation.	Demonstrate use of hydrometer, pH readings.	Hydrometer, pH paper, cider.	By demonstration and Q&A.
13.30–1430	Storage & pasteurisation.	Visit maturation shed, watch pasteurisation process. Reference handout.	Cider, pasteurisers, thermometer, handout.	Discussion and Q&A session.
14.30–1600	Practical juice session.	Learners to wash, pulp & press own juice, using equipment.	Apples, mill, press, containers.	By individual Q&A, by demonstration.
16.00–16.30	Plenary, housekeeping.	Learners to consolidate learning by asking questions, annotate handouts. Feedback to tutor.	Handout, tutor feedback sheet.	By personal feedback session, group feedback, further information etc.

EQUALITY, DIVERSITY & SUSTAINABILITY – discussion as to procedures in other countries, discussion as to comparison of craft cider production and commercial production.
HEALTH & SAFETY – discussion of hygiene, patchulin, pasteurisation and good working practices.
EVERY PERSON MATTERS – Safe? Healthy? Enjoyed/achieved? Achieve economic wellbeing? Make a positive contribution?
TUTOR NOTES – Timing? Content? Practical session? Changes to content/alterations to schedule?

At the end of the course remember to thank your attendees. At this time, perhaps sending them off with a paper *aide memoire* of the other courses you offer might be appropriate.

Charging

When you are putting together your own courses you need to think carefully about your prices. Factors that help determine them might be geographical (you will have a larger catchment if you are near a town or city); popularity (there are always people who want to go on basic courses such as chicken-keeping or beekeeping); and rarity (courses such as blacksmithing are not as common and therefore command a higher price). Overheads affecting the price are insurance, advertising, utilities, stationery and raw materials. The gross profit should reflect the value of your stock in trade, which happens to be your time and expertise. A basic rate of £14 an hour must surely be your minimum, so for a six-hour practical workshop such as the juicing one, I'd be looking at a maximum of six learners at £30 each, yielding £180 for the day – enough to cover my expenses and pay me a decent wage, but not high enough to be off-putting. If I'm inundated with applicants then I can raise my price to say £35 a head. If you are unsure about pricing simply check what your competitors are charging and what the customer gets for it. For a beekeeping experience I used to limit the number to three: four people around a single hive was manageable, and out of the £40 a head I charged I could afford to buy beesuits for my learners.

In a classroom-based presentation with no practical session I usually limited the class size to 12. I kept advertising costs down by using social media and local radio (which was often free), and putting up posters locally. The best day for classes, I found, was Saturday: midweek courses had to be fitted round work and school commitments, and Sunday was regarded by most candidates as a family day. I avoided the school holidays altogether. (The RBC and Adult Education paid me a salary of £20 an hour for teaching their courses.)

Make sure your terms and conditions (especially regarding cancellation!) are printed in full on any print or online brochures and booking forms, and ensure that candidates tick the 'I have read the T&Cs' box, and send an email acknowledgement on receipt of payment.

Volunteers

In the early days I learnt a great deal by volunteering to work for board and lodging on established smallholdings, and in time I was able to pass on my experience to other volunteers. We registered with HelpX and for two years welcomed people of all ages from all over the world to come and help us on our smallholding. I'm sure we learnt as much from them as they did from us!

As hosts you need to be realistic about your expectations – you're not getting a worker who will slave all day every day for nothing. Our volunteers put in four days a week from 10–4; in return they got food, accommodation and on-the-job training and still had time to go and discover Cornwall. For some the curve was steeper than for others: we had two great lads from Spain who had never done any smallholding work and took a while to adjust to our mealtimes, but we all got there in the end. They helped us put up a building, cut fields with machinery, chop and stack firewood and even catch and house a swarm of bees.

Having volunteers is a privilege and both parties want to enjoy the experience. But there's a serious side too. Scrutinise every applicant and ask for references, especially if you're going to allow them in your homes. Get public liability insurance and provide your volunteers with adequate personal protection equipment. Think carefully about what you need them to do, how long their jobs will take, what equipment they'll need and what their incentive is. I personally wouldn't work an eight-hour day for someone who treated me like dirt, never said thank you and didn't offer me lunch or provide protective clothing!

A proper and thorough induction is an absolutely essential start. Introduce yourself and your family and co-workers. Show them their accommodation and make sure they understand how everything works. Feed them. Walk them round the holding explaining the crops, the livestock, what you do and what you hope they will help you with. If they are young make sure they can contact a parent, and get their parents' contact details from them just in case.

Before you shove them out to work, ensure that they know what they are doing and how to do it. Tell them where you are in case they need to ask anything, and tell them when break time is. Even if they are slow, let them finish the job. It will give them confidence, especially if you remember to thank them. Ask them about themselves, what they want to do. Take them to the pub now and again. Lend them bikes so they can get about by themselves. These people are here to learn not just about unfamiliar work but about an unfamiliar culture – you could be making a big difference to their lives.

Markets and Marketing

09

Working hard to produce goods from your smallholding is not, by itself, going to sell anything. The marketplace is where you sell your products whether they are goods such as cider or vegetables or a service such as holiday accommodation. Your market may be local or national or even international, but whether it's accessed at a farmers' market, via a shop or on the internet, you need to make customers aware of what you're selling and where and how they can buy it.

Every smallholding and its goods and services is different, and different products and services lend themselves to different kinds of marketing. For example holiday lets, farm shops, evening classes and leisure attractions such as horse riding all involve the customers actually visiting and using your premises. Other products such as food and drink are portable, and customers can buy them at retail outlets far from their place of origin or online.

Markets

You will probably make a significant proportion of your sales at farmers' markets or food fairs where you get to keep the entire profit minus stall rent. The smaller country produce markets generally held in church halls and run by volunteers are unlikely to sell enough to make the ordeal worth it: I tried the nearest such market when I was selling eggs, honey and plants. It was boring and stuffy and did my head in. I never made enough to cover my time and I lasted eight weeks. I'd never recommend them. Ordinary weekly town markets are also probably not much use to the artisan producers: the majority of stalls are straightforward pricecutters, and the clientele are only after mainstream products at rock-bottom prices.

Farmers' markets and food or craft fairs are the way to go. They are more vibrant and dynamic. The clientele is more affluent and more sophisticated and has come to shop. Farmers' markets also routinely sell alcohol, which most others don't. (Remember, though, that if you want to sell your cider or mead of fruit liqueur at a market you need to check well in advance whether it has a liquor licence. If not, you have 10 working days to apply for a Temporary Events Notice.) Try and ensure you have regular days at markets if possible. Your loyal customers want to know you are always there on a Thursday and may make a special trip just to buy from you. When I sold cider at Padstow Food Fair I tried to book every Friday, Saturday and Sunday in the holiday season. Some markets are better-attended than others: before you commit, pay a visit and talk to one or two of the stallholders. Find your nearest farmers' market(s) on the National Farmers' Retail and Markets Association website **www.farma.org.uk**.

A much more recent development is The Food Assembly, a social enterprise set up in France but now spreading all over Europe to bring customers and local producers together. Customers place their orders online and every week meet the producers at a local venue to collect their orders and socialise. Customers get better food and you, the producer, get a fair price: you set your own price and keep 80 per cent of it. The rest is divided between the local Assembly organisers and the venue. This compares to the 15–25 per cent of the sale price most supermarkets will pay you, so if you're looking for a new sales platform the Food Assembly is well worth considering. For more details visit **www.foodassembly.com**.

In the market itself, even more so than at your own premises, presentation is every bit as important as the goods on display. Your stall will be signed using the same fonts and colours as the signs back at the holding (and I'll say more about branding shortly). Shoppers shop with their senses. They are visually attracted to colourful and interesting stalls. They may also follow the smell of the food or other products on offer. Most will stop in front of your stall to browse. Attractive packaging, clear prices and a friendly and knowledgeable salesperson are important. If you are selling food, a clean apron and neat, tidy hair will inspire confidence. Little samples of food or drink will often result in sales. A simple A5 sheet or brochure with your prices, contact details and order form should be popped into the bag with customers' purchases and also handed out off-stall to generate repeat business. (If yours is a visitor-friendly holding, copies of the same brochure can be left in pubs, cafes, hotel and B&B foyers, the Tourist information centre and elsewhere to direct visitors from outside the district to your premises.)

As a footnote, it's definitely worth selling fresh seasonal produce at a roadside stall (preferably fronted by a safe and convenient lay-by or forecourt!). As with the market, you get the full retail price but you don't even have to pay a stall fee. And if you don't already have and don't want to invest in an open-fronted shed for the purpose, you can even use your actual market stall. But this kind of stall is more than just a generator of cash: its actual takings may not be great, but it makes great public relations. Even passing motorists who have no intention of stopping to buy will clock you, maybe for future reference, maybe not. The point is that every single person in the district will know who and where you are; and if you have something a bit out of the mainstream to offer – you might have a tree or two of russets, say – people will be tempted.

Signage

Perhaps the most obvious and yet most important consideration for even the smallest of rural businesses is signage, because if people can't find you your products are going to sit on the shelf. And a tatty hand-painted board doesn't inspire confidence. Well-made directional signage in a large, clear font will bring customers to your gate; the sign at your entrance should be visible from some distance away to give drivers time to register and should carry your opening hours, phone number and web and email addresses. One thing to beware of is that signage is tightly controlled by planning regulations: you may need permission even to put a sign up at your own front gate, and if you want a brown tourism sign you will have to pay the county council's Highways Department a fortune for the privilege. All signs should be consistent with your branding, of which more below.

Business name

The name you pick for your business is all part of the marketing, and once you've chosen it you're stuck with it, so spend a lot of time thinking about it. In many cases the name will be a simple descriptor of where you are and what you do: Calder Valley Holiday Cottages or Tor Farm Devon Mead leave no-one in any doubt and make internet searches very easy. But christening a business that does many different things, such as a smallholding selling hay, organic vegetables and home-produced beef and pork as well as contracting services is trickier. Perhaps just leave it at the name of the farm? Or combine the name of the farm with a brief description such as Smith's Traditional Meats or Smith's Independent Farm Shop?

The internet plays an important part in choosing a name, too. One way of helping internet customers search for you might be to include your town or county in the domain name. Any search for a holiday cottage in the Calder Valley or mead in Devon will come to your site straight away. Check whether your preferred domain name and email address are already taken before you do anything else: if they're not available you'll have to rethink all the branding you were planning for labels, letterheads, the design of your market stall, signage – the lot. And make your domain name short – it'll be much more memorable. I'm more likely to remember Spotty Dog Cider than North Cornwall Artisan Cider Barn.

Branding

Picking a memorable name and having a consistent theme running throughout your design are important, and if you're in doubt there are plenty of companies that specialise in getting your marketing right. But they'll charge, so before you pay for domain names, social media names, getting a website up and running and so on, think long and hard about branding.

Branding is basically design. Good branding makes your product or service stand out and should be easy to remember, to recognise and most important of all to identify with. Who are your target customers? Are they male or female? What age bracket are they in? Are they locals or tourists? What are their interests? By thinking about how they think, you should be able to create branding to appeal to them.

When I started to look at branding my cider, I decided to aim for the contemporary artisan cider lover and to keep my marketing and sales local to North Cornwall, where it was a 'well-kept secret' produced only in small batches from local apples. It was a great success and basically sold itself at farmers' markets and food fairs.

I approached a linocut artist whose work I admired to design a logo I would use on my website, my bottle labels and all advertising to promote a brand image. The Spotty Dog logo was based on my blue roan spaniel and was executed in black and white (cheap to print and stunningly simple). It appealed to both traditional and contemporary markets and could be adapted as a label design as more varieties of cider were developed. For example, a batch of cider called Seadog utilised the original Spotty Dog head with the addition of a pirate hat with a red ribbon on it. Again, simple and cheap to print but visually attractive. The name Seadog was attractive to customers as we were based on the north coast of Cornwall and sold our cider to local pubs and at local produce markets, and we rapidly sold out.

The internet

The internet is the first place people look these days when searching for any product or service, so the right presence is of critical importance. It's also a good idea to sell as much as you can online so you don't have to share the profit with a third-party retailer. And it all starts with a website.

Website

A website is essential, and it has to be a good one. It should go without saying that your website needs to include every relevant fact about who you are, where you are, what you do and how to get in touch with you – and include it prominently and plainly. If the site carries any material that dates it should be updated assiduously and frequently – you shouldn't be announcing a special offer on alpaca wool throws that expired three weeks ago. If there's anything interactive on it – in particular, an order-form and payment details – make sure it's very, very easy to navigate. The overall design should be very carefully chosen to carry your branding – fonts, colours, logos, weights, borders, every last detail – and to appeal strongly to your chosen demographic: it's no good some whizzkid designer embellishing the site with lasers and glitterballs if your range is mainly composed of hand-turned walking sticks and briar pipes. Use lots of appealing and appropriate pictures. None of this is free. You have to rent a domain name, pay a company to host your site and hire a designer. But it's not optional. It's both your shop window and your shop. If it's done badly it's a complete waste of money. If it's done properly it will repay your investment over and over again.

When someone searches for your product, your website should be top of the list. This means Search Engine Optimisation. Websites compete for attention and ranking in the search engines and people with the knowledge to use SEO will benefit from increased traffic and visibility. But it's complicated and, as with all things computer-related, you can get so bound up in it that you start neglecting the real business of growing and making things.

Email newsletters

Encourage and reward your loyal customers by collecting their email addresses and setting up a newsletter with plenty of exclusive deals and discounts. Exclusivity is something that people will pay for! Keep your mailing list up-to-date but make sure you have the recipient's explicit permission to send them newsletters. Collect addresses for your mailing list by advertising it on social media or in person at shows, fairs and markets.

Social media

It can take a while to get comfortable with social media if you are new to it, but it's worth it. Different social media platforms – Facebook, Twitter, Instagram and so forth – have different demographics, so match your platform to the audience you're trying to reach. Include lots of links to your website (and vice versa). Lack of social media presence invites your customers to question you. A business with a social media presence is automatically viewed as more professional these days. An active presence is even better, so post as regularly as you can. To make it more effective:

- Use pictures. Facebook posts with images win twice as much engagement as those without; on Twitter the figure is 150 per cent.
- Make it real: don't "sell" all the time. Engage with your potential customers warmly and cheerfully.
- Respond to comments and questions as soon as possible. Politely!
- Keep an eye on the analytics. Facebook insights are free. Instagram and Twitter also have analytics tools. Check your posts to see which perform best.
- Avoid personal or political statements. It's a business page. Your customers don't want to know.

If you're unsure about content, look at your competitors. If you are a cidermaker talk about the great harvest (with photos of ripe fruit), or your upcoming wassail (with more details on our website to attract people), or that award you won.

Facebook

This is a great place to start. It has more than a billion daily users, including a sizeable proportion of middle-aged and older people who don't use other platforms as much. You have to register as an individual before you can add a business page.

- Choose your profile picture and cover photo with great care: they need to be clear, sharp and relevant.
- Have a compact and informative 'about' section to describe your business. It's all about personality, so think about the kind of customers you want to attract and try to speak, act and think like your target audience.
- Check the insights tab to see who is viewing your posts. Not getting the response you want? Then perhaps try a paid promotion. Facebook allows you to boost a post for a small charge. And remember to check the analytics after a few days.

Instagram is a very visual medium, great for products that lend themselves to arresting imagery: glasses of sparkling cider, trees just dripping with ripe apples... you get the idea. It's the fastest growing platform and used mainly by younger audiences. They want eye-catching instant images and this tool suits them. My website and social media pages included lots of photographs of my orchard, the trees, fruit and the cider-making process. I also included lots of photos of wildlife. It's not just the cider that people want to buy; it's the lifestyle.

Hashtags is a way of labelling your content with keywords so it is more likely to be seen. The trick is to use the right hashtags. Search 'hashtags for Instagram' or 'Websta' for pointers.

Twitter is very fast-paced and you need to post several times a day, even every half an hour, to make sure your tweets don't get lost in the noise. There is a huge audience available, but it can be a serious drain on your time.

Internet training

If you've read this far and feel overwhelmed by the vocabulary or fear that you don't have the technical ability to embrace social media, get some training. I attended a four-day "build your own website" course using Wordpress. For the first day I was totally out of my depth and drove home with a massive headache. But the next day was better, and although I was slower than most of the other whizzkids on the course I could see my website taking shape and my confidence started to grow.

A few months later, I returned to the centre to learn about social media and how it could help my business. At the time I didn't really know what Facebook was, but within a few weeks, I was posting simultaneously on Facebook and on my website, and yes, my sales were increasing. My advice would be to go on a course if you can, read tutorials and watch videos on the internet and *try* it.

Couriers

There's almost no limit to what couriers will carry these days. In the early days of online shopping, it was very hard indeed to find anyone who would carry liquor in glass bottles, for obvious reasons.

Nowadays couriers will even carry perishable foods, provided they're vacuum-packed. (Always us Royal Mail-approved packaging for glass, by the way. It's not the best, but it's Royal Mail-approved and hence insurable.)

But from your customers' point of view, most couriers offer lousy service. They stay in all morning or all afternoon and if a van actually arrives they daren't take more than 30 seconds to get from armchair to front door or the delivery driver will have scribbled a card and vanished. The drivers are on minimum wage and zero hours contracts, and as far as their bosses are concerned offering the lowest price to their actual customer – i.e., you – easily trumps the service your customer gets. Include a complaints form on your website! It's the only way you can track how well your courier is performing; and don't be afraid to switch couriers. The cheapest is by very definition not the best – if your online customers like your product and feel relaxed about delivery they'll happily pay a little more, especially if you add an explanatory note to your online shop.

Competitions and guidebooks

"Boom, there goes another waste of money. Cancelled my membership of Taste of the **** – since winning Gold last year I have not had one enquiry from a potential customer. The only people that get anything out of these awards are the massive office full of people running the scheme: £115 membership, £36 per product to enter the competition, £70 each for the presentation dinner, more for the worthless little labels to stick on your products, etc. etc. etc... The awards mean nothing, zilch."

An extreme but not uncommon attitude towards promotional competitions – but is it fair? In some industries awards schemes and competitions and medals really do mean something, although to the distributor rather than the public. If you enter your gin, say, in one of the many international competitions that seem to be spreading like rashes, it's rather like a children's gymkhana in that almost every entry gets a rosette of some kind. National distributors will be nosing round looking for suitable brands for the Venezuelan market or the South Korean market – often several distributors from each country – so a rosette really means something.

This is probably not the case as far as smallholders are concerned, unless they're smallholders with ambitions to become somewhat bigger. You may well find that class winner at a more humble horticultural or agricultural show creates more demand than a gold medal at a regional "scheme" – and that it costs an awful lot less to enter!

Guidebooks are a similar case in point. Paying upfront for a listing in a guidebook is one of the oldest scams in the book – the book, in fact, usually doesn't even come out. Don't fall for it! Actually guidebooks generally, even honest ones, hardly matter any more: for all sorts of reasons, not least currency, there is nothing they can do that the internet can't do much better.

Self-sufficiency and sustainability

10

Self-sufficiency isn't just about saving the planet, fantastic aim though that may be. It's much less grand than that: a sustainable industry would be one that was entirely or very nearly self-sufficient, that produced what it promised without devouring resources and damaging the natural environment. And it would be composed of thousands of more or less self-sufficient units.

The UK has a long way to go to make farming sustainable. Even Defra acknowledges in its Strategy for Sustainable Farming and Food that British agriculture has failed to perform economically, environmentally and socially. Farm profitability is at its lowest since the 1930s, and agriculture gobbles up something like £25bn a year of taxpayers' money in direct subsidies (a mere £3bn), grants and exemptions from business rates, fuel duty, VAT, corporation tax and inheritance tax. Despite government initiatives, the rural landscape is still being harmed and farming has become such a low-esteem employer in the eyes of the public that it has to import some 80,000 labourers from Europe.

On a positive note, through, we have an increased understanding of sustainability in farming and processing that reduces both waste and cost. And we know that we can all, both as individuals and as businesses, make small changes that together add up to huge differences.

When John and I moved to our house in Cornwall it was a normal bungalow with an acre of garden. As far as self-sufficiency was concerned it was a blank canvas. Our first job was to install central heating as the house had only electric storage heaters and a draughty wood burner. We decided to install two independent systems: a solid fuel system to use up the large supply of cheap timber we had available, and an LPG system for very cold days and because we had no mains gas. That was the start of our progress towards becoming as self-sufficient as we could be. It just naturally evolved because as we continued to renovate the property it seemed the natural and economic way to go.

As our businesses developed our self-sufficiency developed too. We put clear roof panels in our sheds so we could work under natural light. We recycled rainwater. We downsized to a single vehicle. Soon we were routinely practicing the 3Rs – reduce, reuse and recycle – without really even being aware of it. When we visited other smallholdings or farms we often saw great 3R systems that we shamelessly stole (and were happy to pass on). In this chapter I have concentrated on the main changes you can look at to make both your home and your business more self-sufficient. It's not comprehensive, and your contribution to self-sufficiency can be as much or as little as you wish. Even the smallest changes you can make can mount up to a big difference. For instance, replacing old-school lightbulbs with energy-efficient ones will of course reduce your electricity bills; but had you thought of positioning the mirrors in your house to reflect and therefore double the light so that you don't need as many lights on? A decorative scheme based on pale colours will increase the effect yet further.

I was honoured to be chosen as winner of the Best Individual category at the Cornwall Sustainability Awards in 2014. As I progressed through the selection stages I was amazed that even the smallest changes we had incorporated in our day-to-day lives were highlighted as examples of best practice and innovation: to us they were just common sense. After the recognition I had been accorded John and I continued to develop our aim to walk lightly on the Earth. As a sustainable, local producer I could be honest about what I did and why I did it, and was happy to share my working practices and ethos with my customers.

Organic farming

Organic farming is the first thing that springs to most people's minds when the subject of sustainability crops up, but it's a subject that divides the farming community almost more than any other. Broadly speaking, the term 'organic' is used by its proponents to describe production systems that work with nature, while conventional farming is characterised as trying to conquer nature. Organic farmers by and large refuse to use man-made chemicals of any kind

– no artificial pesticides, herbicides or fertilisers, and strictly limited use of animal vaccines or antibiotics – and rely on crop rotation, soil quality and biodiversity to maintain a healthy growing environment (although it's a myth that organic food is produced with absolutely no pesticides, herbicides or fertilisers. In fact, there is a long list of natural chemicals, additives and animal treatments that organic producers may use). You could say that this was merely a return to traditional pre-war farming, and the Soil Association, founded in Suffolk in 1946 by Lady Eve Balfour and others to promote a return to less intensive, low-input practices, immediately found itself at war with modern mechanised and chemical-dependent farming over the environmental costs of intensive mass production.

Conventional farmers, on the other hand, claim that organic certification allows the use of some very damaging chemicals including sulphur and rotenone (a naturally occurring herbicide, pesticide and piscicide); that food produced organically is no better than that produced by conventional means; and that using manure from animals that are not subject to anti-parasitic treatments and antibiotics as fertiliser is a health hazard. But the strongest argument against organic production is the cost. It makes the land less productive because the permissible density of livestock is lower and because restrictions on the use of fertilisers means arable land has to spend more time fallow; there are higher labour costs; and the fees for registration and compliance are a heavy burden on smaller producers.

Although it was concern for the environment that motivated the organic movement (Lady Balfour's book advocating organic practices was called *The Living Soil*), consumers have also come to regard organic food as healthier and more wholesome. Sales of organic produce started rising sharply in the 1970s and continue to grow: Waitrose says that sales of organic produce in its stores rise by 11 per cent a year – although paradoxically organic production in the UK has dropped every year since 2009 as organic farmers increasingly turn their backs on formal certification. Naturally the consumer wants the best product, but the challenge in these times of austerity is to persuade the consumer that buying the best is better than buying the cheapest. Some organic producers have retreated into niches such as specialist luxury goods – organic baby food and petfood are growth areas – or out-of-season vegetables. Many I know are making Christmas itself their niche, selling organic Brussels sprouts, walnuts, pâté, ducks, turkeys and liqueurs online via distributors such as Big Barn **www.bigbarn.co.uk** and Riverford **www.riverford.co.uk**, which means they can sell a substantial crop to a larger audience for a reasonable price.

There are a number of organic certification schemes around, all compliant with standards set by the UK Register of Organic Food Standards, and you can't call yourself organic without signing up to one or other of them. The largest is operated by the Soil Association; alternatives are Organic Farmers and Growers, Organic Food Federation and Organic Trust Limited. All products claiming to be organic must display a certification number or symbol. There are mandatory inspections, and gaining accreditation can take from one to three years. You can get funding for converting to organic status through the Countryside Stewardship Scheme.

You don't have to be certified organic to promote your products on their green credentials, though. There are other independent assurance schemes such as Red Tractor and, for eggs, the Lion mark, and even if you don't want to or aren't eligible to join them there is very little legally to stop you using expressions in your packaging and marketing such as fresh, natural and wholesome. Trading standards regulations have specific requirements for the correct description of ingredients and dietary values on food packaging, as well as expiry date and point of origin, but in terms of the honesty and credibility of your general and promotional claims, you are the best judge.

Water and sewerage

Britain is immensely profligate with water, to drink, to wash in, to irrigate certain crops with, as a coolant in many industries, to flush away our bodily waste. But although water itself is free, collecting, purifying and distributing it most certainly aren't, and reducing the use of mains water both in the home and on the farm is one of many strands in the pattern of making a smallholding pay. And quite apart from the dent water bills can make in your net profit, mains water isn't entirely sustainable. It's finite, and as the population grows the provision of adequate water and sewerage provision swallows up more and more investment. So for the sake of both your conscience and your wallet, plan to save water.

An obvious starting point is collecting rainwater from roof runoff. It can be used without filtration or chemical treatment for many purposes including irrigation and cleaning. And potentially there's an awful lot of it.

If we take an average monthly rainfall of 90mm and multiply it by the roof area we can harvest water from we will get a volume. For example, a 10m x 4m building has a surface area of 40m² and so would harvest 3,600L in an average month. Obviously therefore the potential exists to collect a large volume of water, and the standard domestic 200L water butt will be sadly inadequate. And a suitable alternative will be expensive.

If you're thinking of installing a serious rainwater harvesting system, look at Building Regulations Part G and H. BS8515 also contains guidance on the design, installation and maintenance of the supply of non-potable water systems. Different coloured pipework must be used to distinguish non-potable supplies from potable, and taps must be clearly labelled and have their handles removed to prevent accidental use. Systems are generally gravity-fed to above-ground circular butyl-lined tanks, stainless steel tanks or lined reservoirs. Filtration systems are required to prevent blockages in pipes and pumping equipment.

The tank or tanks are going to be the most expensive part of the system, and they need to have an overflow capacity to allow for flushing out any debris. Ideally they should be integral to new builds but can be retrofitted. The Environment Agency suggests that costs can start at around £2,500. A quick trawl of the internet produces this complete system: **www.smithsofthedean.co.uk/rainsavers/**

rain-harvesting-system.html. Maintenance is minimal and payback time will depend on the current cost of your water. And for a cheaper DIY approach you can buy suitable piping from any agricultural store or builders' merchant, while ordinary IBCs make durable and inexpensive holding tanks. Second-hand IBCs are easy to come by: for our cider production, I bought food-grade ones from Smith's, which also deals in used fruit juice / concentrate barrels and accessories.

If the cost of installing a serious RHS looks alarming, just consider the possible savings. Charges for mains water range from £1 to £2 per cubic metre and are sure to rise in the future, and there's another charge if your waste water is discharged to a sewerage system. The average person uses 150 litres of water a day; smallholdings use a whole lot more, and even small changes around the house and buildings can make a difference. Using rainwater to flush the toilet could save 34 litres of water a day – that's $12.41m^3$ a year or £25 at £1.94 per cubic metre. And that's just for flushing the loo! Think of all the other on-farm applications you could supply from an RHS and count the savings.

An RHS will also reduce the volume of water entering your slurry stores and grey water tank and washing foul water over your yards. This will help you to comply with Nitrate Vulnerable Zone regulations if you're in an area where nitrate pollution is a problem. More information on this is available from the Environment Agency.

Untreated rainwater contains no chlorine and is therefore ideal for washing machinery, cleaning animal pens, irrigation, hydroponic systems and crop-spraying. But while it's very suitable for root zone watering of horticultural crops, it is not suitable for overhead irrigation on edible salads or fruit crops. Rainwater run-off will contain traces of environmental pollutants, animal and bird faecal matter, and vegetation such as moss, algae and leaves. The roof itself can be a contaminant if it contains asbestos or lead. You may therefore still need filtration and or UV treatment for some crops and for animal and poultry drinking water. The Welfare of Farmed Animals (England) Regulation 2000 requires all animals either to have access to a suitable water supply and be provided with an adequate supply of fresh drinking water each day or be able to satisfy their fluid intake needs by other means. The National Dairy Farm Assurance Scheme (NDFAS) requires water for animal drinking to be fresh and clean. To put this in perspective, one dairy cow requires 60 litres of clean drinking water a day. There are recognised standards set out by the World Health Organisation, and many food assurance schemes have additional requirements that have to be met. The Dairy Hygiene Regulations require water used to wash hands, udders and dairy machinery to be from a potable source. Normally this means mains water, but if you're not on the mains you have a couple of options. You can filter and treat your harvested rainwater so it's fit for consumption, but at a cost (although I would question the necessity of using rainwater for drinking anyway, unless you really are planning to live on an island or somewhere very, very remote). Even water from wells, streams and springs needs treatment: it's totally natural and may well contain iron, peat, nitrates, or even pathogens such as Cryptosporidium, E. coli and Campylobacter. Find out about water standards here: **dwi.defra.gov.uk/consumers/advice-leaflets/standards.pdf**.

A borehole is another option. This isn't simply a matter of drilling a well. The borehole will have to supply enough water of adequate quality for all your needs, which requires testing in advance. The British Geological Survey or the Geological Survey of Northern Ireland can prepare a prognosis for you for a fee, as indeed can many private companies. If both quality and quantity look likely to be sufficient, then you need consent from the Environment Agency or the Scottish Environment Protection Agency for a test hole. If that's all satisfactory you'll probably have to pay around £10,000 to get a working borehole drilled (to a minimum depth of 50m), lined, fitted with a motor pump and connected up, which will all take a few weeks. You may also need to register the borehole. Having said all that, you only need an abstraction licence (again, from the relevant Environment Agency) if you want to extract more than 20,000 litres a day; and once all the work is done and all the form-filling is out of the way you have free source of water that will last for generations.

However – groundwater – whether from boreholes, wells or springs also needs to be checked regularly for safety and you may still need sand filters and UV purifiers just as you would to render rainwater potable.

Producing less foul water and making safe use of what you do produce is another great saving, both environmentally and financially. An obvious start to generating less of it is to stop flushing, whose financial wastefulness I demonstrated above, and use composting toilets instead. The simplest system is no more than a couple of buckets, one for liquids and one for solids, under a wooden stand with seats and lids fitted over them. Commodes, really. Sprinkling sawdust from a handily placed bucket after use will stop them smelling (and if you still feel the need to use any cleaning products, make sure they're environmentally friendly – so no bleach!). Keeping liquids and solids as separate as is feasible is important: type urine separator or diverter into your search engine and while away many a happy hour discovering and evaluating the various methods by which this may be achieved. The urine you collect can be used safely and effectively to activate a compost heap or diluted with five parts water as a soil conditioner: it's 95 per cent water, with the rest made up of nitrogen-rich urea and minerals such as phosphorus and potassium – the very stuff that commercial fertilisers are made of and far too precious to waste.

The solids can be composted separately (but not on the garden heap) for six months to a year in a septic tank or pit under a layer of soil or sawdust and then, like 77 per cent of human sewage, spread over agricultural land or used as garden mulch. It's perfectly safe: according to Water UK, a trade body representing the water and sewerage corporations, "there are no reported cases of human, animal or crop contamination due to the use of sewage sludge on agricultural land". Common sense would however warn against using sewage from households where contraceptive pills, fertility treatments and HRT are being used as the artificial hormones they contain contaminate the run-off from the soil and hence our waterways. (Manure from animals raised on growth hormones is equally harmful in this respect). Read the code of practice at **www.gov.uk/government/publications/sewage-sludge-on-farmland-code-of-practice**. You can find construction plans for a simple compost toilet at **www.compostjunkie.com/composting-toilet-plans.html**; find more upmarket eco-toilets at **dunsterhouse.co.uk**. (Common-or-garden septic tanks are in use even today in the many rural areas that are still without mains sewerage, but have not been considered here because they don't in themselves save any water.)

Finally under this heading, grey water is the run-off from your bath, shower, handbasin, kitchen sink, washing machine and other appliances whose waste water hasn't been in contact with human or animal faeces. It will contain traces of dirt, food, grease, hair and household cleaning products but is nevertheless a safe and even beneficial source of irrigation water; but its nutrients become pollutants if allowed to run off into waterways. It can be used to water trees and gardens provided it doesn't come into direct contact with any fruit and vegetables that might be eaten raw. It should never be held in collection tanks for longer than 24 hours and shouldn't be allowed to puddle during use. Visit **www.greywateraction.org** for information on grey water and safety and also for diagrams and explanations of how to construct grey water reuse systems.

Heating and cooking

More than half of all the money spent on fuel in Britain goes on keeping warm – that is, towards heating, cooking and hot water. These are a particular problem for many smallholders (among other country-dwellers) because so many rural properties aren't on mains gas. Ours was no exception. We found electricity too expensive for heating, so we installed a bulk LPG tank with a condensing boiler and radiators. It was fine for a couple of years but got more and more expensive, so we had a multi-fuel stove with back-boiler and a few more radiators to provide a secondary heating system. The stove also produced enough hot water to install extra hot taps in the kitchen and bathroom, and had hobs capable of boiling a kettle or heating a couple of saucepans. (For serious cooking, though, look at solid fuel ranges like Rayburn, Esse and the legendary Aga. Some produce hot water too, but new ones can cost £4,000.)

Installing a wood or multi-fuel stove is not something you can do yourself unless you have a HETAS qualification – visit **www.hetas.co.uk**. Incorrectly fitted appliances can release lethal carbon monoxide into a room. You'll also invalidate the warranty on the appliance and your insurer may well refuse to reimburse you for any loss or damage, and you will be unable to sell your property without the correct certification. You also need professional advice on where to site the stove and radiators for maximum efficiency, which is a surprisingly technical subject.

What makes this kind of stove of particular significance to the cash-strapped smallholder, though, is that once it's installed you can grow all the fuel you need to keep it going. With the extra hot taps in the kitchen and bathroom and our abundance of timber, it soon became our main source of heating and hot water source, and we only called on the gas boiler either on the coldest of winter days or at the height of summer when all we wanted was hot water.

The stove cost £1,200 all told (although that was in 2007), paid for itself in two years, and then saved us £800 a year. We started off burning about five tonnes a year, but once we had greatly improved our home insulation it fell to four tonnes and we could have reduced it further had we been able to insulate the floors as well. The wood has to be seasoned for a year to prevent tar building up in the flue so we built two wood stores, one for fresh-cut wood and a second, nearer the house, for wood that was seasoned and ready to burn. We harvested coppiced willow as fuel and kindling from a shelter belt we'd planted. It actually proved useless as a windbreak; and serendipitously we found that hornbeam and beech were both much more effective in the hedge and also very good for fuel.

Electricity and lighting

Electricity, mainly for lighting, can account for up to 15 per cent

Case study
Bulworthy Project, Rackenford, Devon
www.bulworthy.uk

Attending a demonstration of charcoal-making turned out to be a life-changing event for shop manager Pete and personnel officer Anna Grugeon, setting them off on a journey that has led to a near-subsistence lifestyle almost completely off the grid.

After attending the demonstration, and already hankering for something more satisfying, the Grugeons cashed in their savings and used the money along with a small inheritance to buy 12 acres of woodland near Bideford in Devon. Living their dream, however, wasn't as simple as it might have been: it took two years of uncertainty and frustration before they finally got planning permission to move their caravan on to the site; but in April 2009 they were settled on their land and able to start the Bulworthy Project in earnest.

The ingoings were minimal: £600 for a second-hand kiln, along with a few hand-tools. The labour, on the other hand, was intense. Small branches and big twigs are more suitable for charcoal than trunk wood, which makes grading and harvesting very laborious. Normally the fuel would be a by-product of forestry, and it might also be a viable use for orchard prunings; but for the Grugeons it was their main crop. The burn itself can take 48 hours, during which the kiln has to be constantly supervised, day and night.

They sold the charcoal they made direct from the site or through local shops, supplying small independent businesses where possible in order to build a business network founded on personal friendships. After only a year in business they established a second income by teaching the skills they had acquired, filling up their courses and special events through social media. And although they had never aimed to be fully self-sufficient, maintaining their lifestyle has relied on producing as much as possible from their land. They either produce or forage much of their food from their fruit trees and bushes; they grow vegetables in a polytunnel; and they keep pigs and chickens.

The Grugeons are out of the caravan now, having built themselves a sustainable house that is off-grid for electricity, being powered by solar and heated by solar and wood. They designed the house themselves, and after having the foundations laid professionally did most of the structural work themselves to save money. They have 960W provided by solar PV panels on a 24-volt DC system. Rainwater is harvested from the roof for toilet and garden use and grey water is recycled via a reed bed filtration system. The savings in water, sewerage and energy as well as food allow Anna and Pete to live a good life on the relatively low income the business produces. In future they plan to rent out a small woodland holiday let, which should eventually outstrip charcoal sales and give them more reliable income.

For more details of the build, see **http://planning.northdevon.gov.uk/liveupload/Scanned%20-%2050k/54230/54230_Sustainable-Building-Statement_120618.pdf** of ordinary household bills, and on a smallholding with all sorts of power-tools and machinery on top of that it makes sense to look at reducing use where possible and even at generating your own.

As we saw at the beginning of this chapter, switching to low-energy lighting and adapting your décor accordingly is the quickest and easiest way you can start to save. The compact fluorescent lamps we are all used to are today being succeeded by the even more efficient LEDs, so use them in as many light-fittings as possible and save up to £35 a year. That should include shed lights and security lights, with movement sensors, rheostats and timers installed to save even more.

Generating electricity on a domestic scale is no big deal these days: every housing estate has a proportion of roofs (not a big enough proportion, though!) sporting those distinctive square black photovoltaic cells to benefit from the feed-in tariff. But using solar PVs to power your smallholding presents a dilemma you can only resolve for yourself. Solar power is DC; the grid is AC. The obvious thing to do, as with any domestic property, is smother all possible roofs – barns and outbuildings as well as the house itself – with PVs and use the FIT payments (which were cut back severely in 2017) to subsidise or with luck completely fund your power consumption. An issue here for anyone really dedicated to self-sufficiency is that half the power you generate will be wasted during inversion to AC. On the other hand, the reduction in FIT payments also triggered a dramatic reduction in the cost of installation – £4,000-5,000 for an average house compared to £11,000 before. Historic and current FIT rates can be found at **www.moneysupermarket.com/gas-and-electricity/feed-in-tariff**.

The alternative – using the electricity you have generated to power both your house and the farmyard directly – is fraught with difficulties and complications. The grid supplies alternating current at 240 volts, and that's what almost all appliances are designed to run on. The low-voltage direct current supplied by PV cells – typically 12 or 24 volts – is fine for lighting and low-voltage appliances such as phone chargers and portable TVs that you'd expect to find in a caravan. For serious use, though, it has to be inverted to AC

240V; and as we've seen, you lose so much power during the process that you need acres of solar collectors as well as mountains of batteries to be able to supply a reasonable demand. For more information visit **www.bimblesolar.com**, a specialist off-grid provider supplying mainly boats and caravans; and **groups.yahoo.com/neo/groups/12VDC_Power/info** is a Google group that specialises in 12, 24 or 48 volt systems and applications.

Solar panels are not the only way of generating your own power. Large wind turbines are responsible for providing more and more of the nation's electricity but scaled-down versions are generally only regarded as powerful enough for single-use appliances such as borehole pumps or on campsites. Integrated systems using solar with small wind turbines as back-up can prove highly effective, though. Vertical axis turbines, as at **www.leadingedgepower.com**, are much less obtrusive than the usual horizontally-mounted version with the propeller-type blades and are supposedly more efficient too.

There's a third option, too, more efficient than either sun or wind if sited correctly, and that's water. Provided there's a fast-running year-round stream on your holding you can install one of any number of devices – Archimedes screw or paddle wheels for low-pressure flows on fairly flat land, submerged turbines for high-pressure mountain streams and larger rivers. Naturally, it's not as simple as it sounds: piping, small dams, millponds and other works might be necessary and will be pricey; you'll almost certainly need planning permission; and you still have the question of inverting DC to AC to resolve. For more on this and other issues related to sustainable energy visit **www.energysavingtrust.org.uk**.

Off-grid living

Living entirely off the grid might be seen as a somewhat extreme version of sustainability – veganism to the smallholder's vegetarianism, as it were. But a growing number of people are choosing complete self-sufficiency, as far as it is possible; some out of conviction, some because it's the only way they can afford to live on their holdings, and some because their holdings are so remote there are simply no mains services, or at least getting connected would cost a fortune.

Living off-grid is not an easy option. You have to be mentally, physically and financially fit to make a home, deal with your waste (all sorts of waste), source all your own utilities and make a living while you're at it. And it's important not to allow yourself to become isolated: keeping at least some lines of communication open is not only vital to your mental wellbeing but also of great practical value. One day, and probably sooner rather than later, you're going to need the help of an extra pair of hands or two.

If you have any doubts then start small, and perhaps go and stay in an existing off-grid community such as Tinker's Bubble in Somerset or Brithdir Mawr in Powys for a while to see what it really entails. These communities are few and far between because of draconian planning restrictions and, let's be honest, a suspicious streak about alternative lifestyles among the local establishment. Tinker's Bubble, a small woodland community in Somerset, was started in 1994 but has only ever had temporary planning permission. There are only a small number of permanent residents, but the community will accept new members and is a WWOOF host (Worldwide Opportunities on Organic Farms). Run as an environmentally friendly enterprise, electricity is 12V, with spring water and composting toilets. Its income comes entirely from the land, including sales of firewood, charcoal, apple juice, jam and woodland produce. There is a communal roundhouse and small sleeping units. The whole community shares chores and members work mainly outdoors. There are open days for you to come and see the set-up for yourself, and some short courses are available. For more details visit **www.tinkersbubble.org**.

The Centre for Alternative Technology in Maccynlleth, Powys, **www.cat.org.uk**, is an absolute Aladdin's cave of innovative solutions in housing, energy generation, waste disposal and all other construction-related alternatives. A visit is enthralling and thought-provoking even if you're not particularly interested in the topic. It runs a number of courses for people who want to go off-grid.

The Centre for Sustainable Energy, **www.cse.org.uk**, offers practical help, guidance and advice to sustainable energy projects from its base in Bristol. Other must-visit sites are:
www.thegreenlivingforum.net/forum,
www.bulworthyproject.org.uk/selfbuild/
www.ben-law.co.uk
www.self-build.co.uk/eco-house-budget
www.cropthornehouse.co.uk/design/

Appendix

11

Appendix I: Agricultural Occupancy Conditions

An Agricultural Occupancy Condition (AOC) obliges the occupier of the land to use it only for defined agricultural and ancillary activities and effectively restricts the building of housing in the countryside. Until 2004, this meant that planning for residential use in the countryside was strictly opposed, unless it was to provide housing for agricultural, horticultural or forestry workers or to support the installation of travellers' sites. Most planning applications were therefore subject to the constraints of the AOC, and occupations such as making cheese or cider or repairing agricultural machinery did not fit the definition of agriculture.

Since 2004, Planning Policy Statement 7 has made it possible to build a dwelling in the countryside associated with other rural enterprises. PPS7 is a bit vague and you will be advised to take some professional guidance on this, but businesses such as quarrying, education in land-based skills and wildlife conservation all appear to fulfil the brief, as do tourism and services ancillary to agriculture. Planners usually insist that whatever enterprise is undertaken, it must have an essential link to the countryside if the applicant wishes to dwell or build a dwelling on the property: so, green burial grounds and raptor centres – yes; catteries or agricultural contractors – no.

If you wish to buy an existing dwelling that is subject to an AOC, your solicitor will make you aware of the wording of the AOC, and ask you how you intend to fulfil the condition. Wording may vary slightly, but typically will read: *The occupation of the dwelling shall be limited to a person solely or mainly employed, or last employed, in the locality, in agriculture or in forestry, or a widow or widower of such a person, and to any resident dependents.* Keeping a couple of sheep or some chickens is not going to qualify: the occupier's main earnings must come from agriculture, forestry or horticulture. The only exception is if you are a retired farmer or farmworker or the widow or widower of one and that your main income or that of your deceased spouse came from agriculture.

Living with an AOC can be very stressful – you are liable, for instance, to unannounced inspections by council enforcement officers. There are, however, two ways of getting out of it. First, the AOC will be lifted if you can show that there is no existing need for agricultural workers' dwellings in the area. To do this you need to put the property up for sale at a price that reflects the limitations of the AOC (normally a third of market value price). If there are no takers within 18 months –two years, and if you can produce evidence that other properties under an AOC have been put on the market and failed to sell, the district council will consider a planning application for the revocation of the AOC. Alternatively, you can apply for a Certificate of Existing Lawful Use or Development if you can prove that the dwelling has been continuously breaching the terms and conditions of the AOC for at least ten consecutive years. A Certificate of Lawful Existing Use is difficult to get and you will need the advice of a solicitor or specialist surveyor. The costs can be high and the process lengthy and stressful.

Appendix II: Food hygiene – a guide for businesses

Food hygiene in retail is governed by an extensive and complicated regulatory catalogue that is really a specialist subject in its own right. Luckily, the Food Standards Agency has published a very useful booklet that summarises and simplifies the regime for busy people who might not necessarily be well-versed in legal language and concepts. It is mainly intended as guidance to retailers but much of the information is equally relevant to food processing. Here we offer a précis that will help guide you through the undergrowth.

Food hygiene – a guide for businesses

This booklet tells you about the key laws that affect your business, what they require you to do and how they are enforced. The most important are Regulation (EC) 852/2004 on the hygiene of foodstuffs and The Food Hygiene (England) Regulations 2006 and equivalents. These set out the basic hygiene requirements for all aspects of your business, from your premises and facilities to the personal hygiene of your staff.

Food safety management procedures

You must put in place food safety management procedures based on the principles of Hazard Analysis and Critical Control Points. You must keep up-to-date documents and records relating to your procedures and review your procedures if you change what you produce or how you work. You must write these procedures down, update them as needed and keep records that can be checked by your local authority. The regulations are designed to be flexible, so these procedures can be in proportion to the size of your business and the type of work that you do. This means that many small businesses will have very simple procedures and records.

What is a hazard?

When we are talking about hazards in relation to food, a hazard is something that could mean that food will not be safe to eat. Food safety hazards can be:

- Microbiological – involving harmful bacteria, e.g. when certain food is kept out of the fridge for too long and bacteria grow in it.
- Chemical – involving chemicals getting into food, e.g. cleaning products or pest control chemicals.
- Physical – involving objects getting into food, e.g. broken glass or pieces of packaging.

How do I put in place food safety management procedures?

You can develop your own procedures based on the principles of HACCP. Alternatively you can use a pack produced by the FSA or your local authority, or a food industry guide recognised by the FSA, to help you comply with the law. These procedures may not be necessary in businesses with very simple processes. In this case, businesses can comply with the legal requirement by following good hygiene practice. They would still need to comply with the other requirements described in this booklet. Contact your local authority for advice.

General requirements

You must keep your premises clean and in good repair and condition. The layout, design, construction, site and size of your premises must:

- Allow adequate maintenance, cleaning and or disinfection.
- Avoid or minimise airborne contamination.
- Provide enough working space for you to carry out all tasks hygienically.
- Protect against the build-up of dirt, contact with toxic materials, shedding of particles into food and forming of condensation or mould on surfaces.
- Allow good food hygiene practices, including protection against contamination and, in particular, pest control.
- Provide, where necessary, suitable conditions for handling

and storing food while keeping it at appropriate temperatures which should be monitored and, where necessary, recorded.

Handwashing facilities and toilets

You must have an adequate number of flush lavatories connected to an effective drainage system. Toilets must not open directly into rooms where you handle food. Toilets must have enough ventilation, either natural or mechanical. You must have an adequate number of washbasins, suitably located and used only for cleaning hands. Washbasins must have hot and cold running water, soap and materials for hygienic drying. Where necessary, you should have a separate sink for washing food.

Other requirements

- You must have enough ventilation, either natural (windows or vents) or mechanical (extractor fans). Ventilation systems must allow access to clean or replace filters and other parts.
- You must have adequate lighting, either natural daylight and or artificial.
- Drainage facilities must be adequate for the purpose intended. They must be designed and constructed to avoid the risk of contamination.
- You must provide facilities for staff to change their clothes where necessary.
- You must not store cleaning chemicals and disinfectants in areas where food is handled.

Rooms where food is prepared or processed

There are special requirements for rooms where you prepare or process food. The design and layout of the room must allow good food hygiene practices including protection against contamination between and during tasks. Floors and walls must be maintained in a sound condition and be easy to clean and disinfect. Floors need to be made of materials that are impervious, non-absorbent, washable and non-toxic. Floors must allow adequate drainage. Walls must be smooth up to a height appropriate for the work you do.

Ceilings and overhead fixtures must be constructed and finished in a way that prevents dirt from building up and reduces condensation, the growth of undesirable mould and the shedding of particles.

Windows and other openings must be constructed to prevent dirt from building up. Windows and other openings that open to the outdoors must be fitted, where necessary, with insect-proof screens that can be removed for cleaning. Where open windows would cause contamination, they must remain closed and fixed while you are producing food. Doors must be easy to clean and disinfect. The surfaces of doors must be smooth and non-absorbent.

Surfaces of equipment in areas where food is handled, particularly those that are touched by food, must be maintained in a sound condition and be easy to clean and disinfect. They must be made of smooth, washable, corrosion-resistant and non-toxic materials.

You must have an adequate supply of hot and cold water and adequate facilities for cleaning, disinfecting and storing utensils and equipment. These facilities need to be made of corrosion-resistant materials and be easy to clean.

You must have adequate facilities, where necessary, for washing food. Every sink for washing food must have an adequate supply of hot and cold water that must be potable. These facilities must be kept clean and, where necessary, disinfected.

Transport

Vehicles and / or containers used to transport food must be kept clean and maintained in good repair and condition to protect food from contamination. They must be designed and constructed to allow adequate cleaning and disinfection.

Items used to hold food (e.g. boxes) in vehicles and or containers must not be used for transporting anything other than food where this may cause contamination. Where vehicles and or containers are used for transporting anything other than food, or for transporting different types of food at the same time, you must separate the products effectively. When vehicles or containers have been used for transporting anything other than food or for transporting different foods, you must clean effectively between loads to avoid the risk of contamination. Food in vehicles or containers must be placed and protected in a way that minimises the risk of contamination.

Where necessary, vehicles and containers used for transporting food must be capable of keeping it at appropriate temperatures which can be monitored.

Equipment

All items, fittings and equipment that food touches must be:

- Cleaned effectively disinfected frequently enough to avoid any risk of contamination.
- Made of appropriate materials and kept in good condition in a way that minimises risk of contamination and enables them to be kept clean and disinfected, except for non-returnable containers and packaging.
- Installed in a way that allows adequate cleaning of the equipment and the surrounding area.
- Fitted where necessary with an appropriate control device (e.g. a temperature sensor).

Food waste

You must remove food waste and other rubbish from rooms where food is present as quickly as possible. You must put food waste and other rubbish in containers that can be closed. These containers must be of appropriate construction, kept in sound condition and be easy to clean and disinfect. You must have adequate facilities for storing and disposing of food waste and other rubbish. Stores for waste must be designed and managed in a way that enables them to be kept clean and free of pests. You must get rid of all waste in a hygienic and environmentally-friendly way in accordance with legislation – contact your local authority for details. The waste must not be a direct or indirect source of contamination e.g. touching surfaces that food is prepared on or attracting pests.

Water supply

You must have an adequate supply of potable water. Where non-potable water is used in your business, it must circulate in a separate, identified system. It must not connect with, or be able to get into, the systems for potable water. If recycled water is used in processing or as an ingredient, it must not present a risk of contamination.

- Ice that is touched by food, or may contaminate food (including drinks), must be made from potable water. Ice must be made, handled and stored in ways that protect it from contamination.
- Steam that is used directly in contact with food must not contain any substance that presents a hazard to health or is likely to contaminate the food.
- If you heat food in hermetically sealed containers, you must make sure that the water you use to cool the containers after heat treatment is not a source of contamination.

Personal hygiene and fitness for work

Everyone working in a food-handling area must maintain a high level of personal cleanliness and wear suitable, clean and, where necessary, protective clothing. Staff should keep hair tied back and wear a suitable head covering, e.g. hat or hairnet, when preparing food. Staff should not wear watches or jewellery when preparing food (except a wedding ring). Staff should not touch their face and hair, smoke, spit, sneeze, eat or chew gum when they are handling food.

You must not allow anyone to handle food or enter a food-handling area if they are suffering from or carrying a disease likely to be transmitted through food; have infected wounds, skin infections or sores; or have diarrhoea. Anyone working in a food business who is affected by any of these and is likely to come into contact with food through their work must tell the business owner or manager immediately about the illness or symptoms and, if possible, what has caused them. Staff with diarrhoea or vomiting should not return to work until they have had no symptoms for 48 hours.

Handwashing

Effective handwashing is extremely important to help prevent harmful bacteria from spreading from people's hands to food, work surfaces, equipment etc. Make sure that all staff who work with food wash their hands properly:

- When entering the food handling area, e.g. after a break or going to the toilet.
- Before preparing food.
- After touching raw food, such as meat/poultry, fish, eggs and unwashed fruit and vegetables.
- After handling food waste or emptying a bin.
- After cleaning.
- After blowing their nose.
- After touching phones, light switches, door handles and cash registers, or other surfaces that could come into contact with staff handling raw food.

Don't forget that staff should dry hands thoroughly on a disposable towel – harmful bacteria can spread more easily if your hands are wet. Use the disposable towel to turn off the tap.

Food

You must not accept raw materials or ingredients or any other material used in processing products if they are known to be, or might reasonably be expected to be, contaminated in a way that means the final product would be unfit for human consumption. You must store raw materials and all ingredients in appropriate conditions designed to prevent deterioration and protect them from contamination.

You must have adequate procedures to control pests and to prevent domestic animals from getting into places where food is prepared, handled or stored. If you run a B&B or another type of food business from a domestic premises, you must have adequate procedures to prevent pets from causing contamination in your kitchen (e.g. with thorough cleaning).

Hazardous and or inedible substances must be labelled adequately and stored in separate and secure containers.

Temperature

You must not keep food at temperatures that might cause a risk to health. The cold chain must not be interrupted for foods that rely on temperature control for their safety. However, you are allowed to have food outside temperature control for limited periods of time to allow you to prepare, transport, store, display and serve food as long as this does not cause a risk to health.

If you manufacture, handle and wrap processed food, you must have suitable rooms large enough to store raw materials and processed materials separately, and enough separate refrigerated storage.

If food is going to be kept or served at chilled temperatures, you must cool it as quickly as possible after cooking (or other heat processing), or after final preparation if you are not heating the food, to a temperature that does not cause a risk to health.

Cold food must be kept at 8°C or below. This is a legal requirement in England, Wales and Northern Ireland, and is recommended in Scotland. In Scotland, food must be kept in a fridge or cool ventilated place. Hot food must be kept at 63°C or above. This is a legal requirement throughout the UK. When you reheat food, make sure that it is steaming hot all the way through. In Scotland, there is a legal requirement for reheated food to reach at least 82°C.

When you are serving or displaying food, you can keep it out of temperature control for a limited period. Cold food can be kept above 8°C for up to four hours. You should only do this once. If any food is left after this time you should throw it away or keep it at 8°C or below until it is used. Hot food can be kept below 63°C for up to two hours but you should only do this once. If any food is left after this time you should reheat it till steaming hot and put it back into hot holding, or cool it as quickly as possible to 8°C or below or throw it away. It is very important not to keep food out of temperature control for longer than these times.

If you defrost food you must do it in a way that minimises the risk of harmful bacteria growing or toxins forming. While you are defrosting food you must keep it at a temperature that would not result in a risk to health. Where liquid coming from defrosting food may present a risk to health (e.g. when defrosting raw meat) you must drain it off adequately. Following defrosting, food must be handled in a way that minimises the risk of harmful bacteria growing or toxins forming (e.g. keeping it in the fridge).

Wrapping and packaging

If you wrap or package food as part of your business (including selling food to take away) then you must follow these requirements:

Materials used for wrapping and packaging must not be a source of contamination or stored where they might be exposed to a risk of contamination.

You must wrap and package in a way that avoids contamination. If you re-use any wrapping and or packaging material for food, it must be easy to clean and disinfect.

Training

Food businesses must make sure that staff who handle food are supervised, instructed and or trained in food hygiene in a way that is appropriate for the work they do. The person or people responsible for developing and maintaining the business's food safety management procedures, based on the principles of Hazard analysis and critical control points (HACCP), must have received adequate training to enable them to do this.

There is no legal requirement to attend a formal training course or get a qualification, although many businesses may want their staff to do so. The necessary skills can also be obtained in other ways such as on-the-job training, self-study or relevant prior experience. Packs produced by the FSA and industry guides to good hygiene practice can also help to train you and your staff.

Movable and temporary premises

Movable and/or temporary premises include marquees, market stalls, mobile vans, vending machines and private homes where food is regularly prepared to be sold or given to the public, e.g. B&Bs. Premises and vending machines must be positioned, designed, constructed and kept clean and maintained in good repair and condition in a way that avoids the risk of contamination, particularly from animals and pests. These requirements all apply to moveable and temporary premises.

Enforcement of the law

Local authorities are responsible for enforcing food hygiene laws and enforcement officers may visit your business premises to inspect them. These officers might come on a routine inspection or they might visit because of a complaint. They have the right to enter and inspect your premises at any reasonable time and will usually come without telling you first. When they think it is necessary, officers can take enforcement action to protect the public. This can include:

- Taking samples of food.
- Inspecting your records.
- Writing you a letter asking you to put right any problems.
- Serving a formal legal notice that sets out certain things you must do, or forbidding you from using certain processes, premises or equipment.
- Recommending a prosecution in serious cases.

Good food hygiene

Good food hygiene is essential for you to make or sell food that is safe to eat. So even though there might not be a specific legal requirement behind each tip in this section, it is still very important for you and your staff to understand what good food hygiene is and to follow this advice. Good food hygiene helps you to obey the law, reduce the risk of food poisoning among your customers and protect your business's reputation.

Good food hygiene is all about controlling harmful bacteria that can cause serious illness. The four main things to remember for good hygiene are the 4 Cs:

- Cross-contamination
- Cleaning
- Chilling
- Cooking

Cross-contamination is when bacteria are spread between food, surfaces or equipment. It is most likely to happen when raw food touches or drips on to ready-to-eat food, equipment or surfaces. Cross-contamination is one of the most common causes of food poisoning. To avoid it:

- Clean and disinfect work surfaces, chopping boards and equipment thoroughly before you start preparing food and after you have used them to prepare raw food.
- Use different equipment (including chopping boards and knives) for raw meat/poultry and ready-to-eat food unless they can be heat disinfected in, for example, a commercial dishwasher.
- Wash your hands before preparing food.
- Wash your hands thoroughly after touching raw food.
- Keep raw and ready-to-eat food apart at all times, including packaging material for ready-to-eat food.
- Store raw food underneath ready-to-eat food in the fridge. If possible, use separate fridges for raw and ready-to-eat food.
- Provide separate working areas, storage facilities, clothing and staff for the handling of ready-to-eat food.
- Use separate machinery and equipment, such as vacuum packing machines, slicers and mincers, for raw and ready-to-eat food.
- Separate cleaning materials, including cloths, sponges and mops, should be used in areas where ready-to-eat foods are stored, handled and prepared.
- Make sure that your staff knows how to avoid cross-contamination.

Effective cleaning gets rid of bacteria on hands, equipment and surfaces and helps prevent harmful bacteria from spreading on to food. You should do the following things:

- Make sure your staff wash and dry their hands thoroughly before handling food.
- Clean and disinfect food areas and equipment between tasks, especially after handling raw food.

- Clear away used equipment, spilt food etc. as you work and clean work surfaces thoroughly. Use cleaning products that are suitable for the job and follow the manufacturer's instructions. Disinfection products should meet BS EN standards. Check product labels for either of these codes: BS EN 1276 or BS EN 13697.
- Do not let food waste build up.

Chilling food properly helps to stop harmful bacteria from growing. Some food needs to be kept chilled to keep it safe, for example food with a use-by date, cooked dishes and other ready-to-eat food such as prepared salads and desserts. It is very important not to leave these types of food standing around at room temperature, so make sure you do the following things:

- Check chilled food on delivery to make sure it is cold enough.
- Put food that needs to be kept chilled in the fridge straight away.
- Cool cooked food as quickly as possible and then put it in the fridge.
- Keep chilled food out of the fridge for the shortest time possible during preparation.
- Check regularly that your fridge and display units are cold enough.

Thorough cooking kills harmful bacteria in food, so it is extremely important to make sure that food is cooked properly. When cooking or reheating food, always check that it is steaming hot all the way through. It is especially important to make sure that you cook poultry, pork, rolled joints and minced meat products such as burgers and sausages thoroughly because they could be sheltering bacteria in the middle. They should not be served pink or rare and should be steaming hot all the way through. Whole cuts of beef and lamb, such as steaks, cutlets and whole joints, can be served pink/rare as long as they are fully sealed on the outside.

Good food hygiene is good for business

If you serve or supply food direct to the public, you may be covered by the Food Hygiene Rating Scheme. This means that when your business is inspected, you will be given a hygiene rating from 0-5. In Scotland you will be given a Pass or Improvement Required result under the Food Hygiene Information Scheme. You will be given a sticker/certificate with your rating or result that you can display to show customers how good your hygiene standards are. They will also be able to look you up on the FSA website at **www.food.gov.uk/ratings**.

What help can I get?

If you would like advice about obeying food hygiene law, get in touch with your local authority. If you run a small catering business there are FSA packs available to help you put in place food safety management procedures based on the principles of HACCP. The FSA has also produced guidance documents on the food hygiene regulations, which you can read on **www.food.gov.uk/business-industry**. Guidance for businesses handling raw and ready-to-eat food can be found at **www.food.gov.uk/business-industry/guidance/hygguid**.

There are also a number of FSA publications including Starting Up – Your First Steps to Running a Catering Business at **www.food.gov.uk/starting-up** and Food Law Inspections and Your Business at **www.food.gov.uk/food-law-inspections**. Guides produced by the food industry also give advice on how to comply with food hygiene regulations. Using the guides is voluntary, but they are officially recognised by the government and enforcement officers are required to take them into account when assessing whether businesses comply with the regulations. For details visit **www.food.gov.uk/industryguides**.

Directory of Services and Suppliers

Advisory Organisations

ADAS
Spring Lodge, 172 Chester Road, Helsby, WA6 0AR
Tel + 44 (0) 333 0142950
www.adas.co.uk

Country Land and Business Association (CLA)
16 Belgrave Square, London, SW1X 8PQ
Tel +44 (0)20 7235 0511
www.cla.org.uk

Countryside Agency (NOW: Natural England)
County Hall, Spetchley Road
Worcester ,WR5 2NP
Tel +44 (0) 300 060 3900
www.gov.uk/government/organisations/natural-england

DEFRA
www.gov.uk/government/organisations/deparment-for-environment-food-rural-affairs

Farming Advice Service
www.gov.uk/government/groups/farming-advice-service

Farming and Countryside Education (FACE)
Stoneleigh Park, Warwickshire CV8 2LG
Tel +44 (0) 845 838 7192
www.face-online.org.uk

Linking Environment and Farming (LEAF)
Tel: +44 (0)247 6413 911
www.leafuk.org

National Farm Attractions Network (NFAN)
105 The Mount, York, YO24 1GY
Tel +44 (0) 1904 615059
www.farmattractions.net

Tenant Farmers Association
5 Brewery Court, Theale, Reading, Berkshire, RG7 5AJ
Tel +44 (0) 118 930 6130
www.tfa.org.uk

Associations, Clubs and Societies

British Beekeepers Association
National Beekeeping Centre
Stoneleigh Park
Kenilworth, Warwickshire, CV8 2LG

www.bbka.org.uk
Tel + 44 (0) 871 362 0138

Central Scotland Smallholders
http://smallholders.webs.com/

Cheshire Smallholders Association
www.cheshiresmallholders.org.uk

Derbyshire Smallholders Association
www.derbyshiresmallholders.co.uk

Devon Association of Smallholders
Tel + 44 (0) 1271 282 002
www.devonsmallholders.co.uk

Dyfed Smallholders Association
www.dyfedsmallholders.org.uk

East Essex Smallholders Group
eastessexsmallholders.blogspot.co.uk

East Kent Smallholders
Facebook: East Kent Smallholders Assoc

Fenland Smallholders
Dowse Farm, Holbeach Drove Gate, Holbeach Drove,
Lincolnshire, PE12 0RX
www.fenlandsmallholders.org.uk

Guernsey Smallholders
www.guernseysmallholders.weebly.com

Kent Smallholders
www.kentsmallholders.co.uk

Lincolnshire Smallholding and Self Sufficiency Club
Facebook: Lincolnshire Smallholding and Self-Sufficiency Club

National Association of Cider Makers Ltd
The Bounds
Much Marcle, Ledbury
Herefordshire, HR8 2NQ
http://cideruk.com/
Tel + 44 (0) 1531 660832

National Farmers Union Agriculture House
Stoneleigh Park, Stoneleigh,
Warwickshire, CV8 2TZ
Tel +44 (0) 24 7685 8500
www.nfuonline.com

Norfolk Smallholders Training Group
www.nstg.org.uk

North Pennines Smallholders
www.northpennines smallholders.co.uk

North Shropshire Smallholders
www.northshrop-smallholder.co.uk

North Yorkshire Smallholders Society
www.nysmallholders.co.uk

Northumbria Smallholders Association
www.northumbriasmallholders.co.uk

Orchards Live, Jane Schofield (secretary), Lewdon Farm,
Black Dog, Crediton, Devon, EX17 4QQ
www.orchardslive.org.uk

Romford Smallholder Society
www.romfordsmallholders.wixsite.com/growyourown

Scottish Smallholders Association
www.scottishsmallholder.com

Shropshire Smallholders Group
Facebook: Shropshire Smallholders Chat

Small Farm Training Group (Sussex)
www.sftg.co.uk

Somerset Smallholders Association
www.smallholdersomerset.com

Suffolk Smallholders Association
www.suffolksmallholders.co.uk

Surrey Smallholders Association
https://surreysmallholders.org/

West Sussex Smallholders Club
www.westsussexsmallholder-sclub.org.uk

Equipment and Suppliers

Adam's Apples
Egremont Barn, Payhembury, Honiton, Devon, EX14 3JA
www.adamsappletrees.co.uk
www.talatonplants.co.uk
Tel +44 (0) 1404 841166

Bateson Trailers
Doodfield Works, Windlehirst Road, Marple, Stockport, SK6 7EN
www.batesontrailers.com
Tel +44 (0) 161 426 0500

Bottle Company South
Pixash Business Centre, Pixash Lane, Keynsham, Bristol, BS31 1TP
www.bottlecompanysouth.co.uk
Tel +44 (0) 117 986 9667

Brinsea Incubators
32–33 Buckingham Road
Weston Industrial Estate
Weston Super Mare, BS2,4 9BG
www.brinsea.co.uk
Tel +44 (0) 345 226 0120

Brouwland
Korspelsesteenweg 86, 3581
Beverlo, Belgium
www.brouwland.com
Tel +32 11 40 14 08

Deacon's Nursery
Moor View, Godshill, Isle of
Wight, PO38 3HW
www.deaconsnurseryfruits.co.uk
Tel + 44 (0) 1983 840750

Defenders
C/O Wye Bugs, Occupation Road,
Wye, Ashford, TN25 5EN
www.defenders.co.uk
Tel + 44 (0) 1233 813130

Dobies
Long Road, Paignton, Devon,
TQ4 7SX
www.dobies.co.uk
Tel + 44 (0) 333 240 5933

Far Gro
Far Gro Ltd, Vinery Fields
Arundel Road (A27), Poling
Arundel, West Sussex, BN18 9PY
www.fargro.co.uk
Tel + 44 (0) 1903 721591

First Tunnels Ltd
Dixon Street, Barrowford,
Lancashire, BB9 8PL
www.firsttunnels.co.uk
Tel +44 (0) 1282 601253

Goat Nutrition
Units BandC, Smarden Business
Estate, Monks Hill, Smarden,
Ashford, Kent, TN27 8QL
www.gnltd.co.uk
Tel +44 (0) 1233 770780

Hyperdrug Pharmaceuticals
Station Industrial Estate
Middleton in Teesdale, Barnard
Castle, Co Durham, DL12 0NG
www.hyperdrug.co.uk
Tel +44 (0) 1833 641112

Ifor Williams Trailers
The Old Station, Bridge Street,
Corwen, Denbighshire,
LL21 0AD
www.iwt.co.uk
Tel +44 (0) 1490 412527

Jongia UK Ltd
23 Prospect Lane, Solihull,
B91 1HN
www.jongiauk.com
Tel +44 (0) 121 744 4844

Keepers Nursery
Gallants Court, Gallants Lane,
East Farleigh, Maidstone, Kent,
ME15 0LE
www.keepers-nursery.co.uk
Tel +44 (0) 1622 326465

Moorlands
Stable Cottage, Adlestrop
Morton-in-Marsh, Glos,
GL56 0YN
www.cheesemaking.co.uk
Tel +44 (0) 1608 658855

National Bee Supplies
Unit 14–15 Hambledown Road,

Exeter Road Industrial Estate,
Okehampton, EX20 1UB
www.beekeeping.co.uk
Tel +44 (0) 1837 54084

Nisbets Catering Equipment
Nisbets PLC, Fourth Way,
Avonmouth, Bristol, BS11 8TB
www.nisbets.co.uk
Tel +44 (0) 845 140 5555

Northern Polytunnels
Mill Green, Waterside Road,
Colne, Lancashire, BB8 0TA
www.northernpolytunnels.co.uk
Tel +44 (0) 1282 873120

Rutland Electric Fencing
Woodstream Europe Ltd,
8 Lands End Way, Oakham,
Rutland, LE15 6RF
www.rutland-electric-fencing.co.uk
Tel +44 (0) 1572 722 558

SCH Supplies
Holbrook, Ipswich, Suffolk,
IP9 2PT
www.schsupplies.co.uk
Tel +44 (0) 1473 328272

Smallholder Feeds
The Smallholder Range, Norfolk
Mill, Shipdham, Thetford,
Norfolk, IP25 7SD
www.smallholderfeed.co.uk
Tel +44 (0) 1362 822900

Smallholding Equipment
Philleyholme Mill, Mill Lane,
Hawkchurch, Axminster, Devon,
EX13 5XQ
www.smallholdingequipment.co.uk
Tel +44 (0) 1297 678998

Solway Feeders Ltd
Main Street, Dundrennan,
Kirkcudbright, DG6 4QH
www.solwayfeeders.com
Tel +44 (0) 1557 500253

Supplies for Smallholdings
Bridge Farm, Fen Road,
Donington, Spalding, Lincs,
PE11 4XE
www.suppliesforsmallholders.co.uk
Tel +44 (0) 7981 336098

Smiths of the Forest of Dean
Station Road, Coleford, Glos,
GL16 8PZ
www.smithsofthedean.co.uk
Tel +44 (0) 1594 833308

Thompson and Morgan
Poplar Lane, Ipswich, IP8 3BU
www.thompson-morgan.com
Tel +44 (0) 844 573 1818

E. H. Thorne Beehives Ltd
Beehive Business Park, Rand,
Nr Wragby, Market Rasen,
LN8 5NJ
www.thorne.co.uk
Tel +44 (0) 1673 858 555

Verm-X

Paddocks Farm Partnership Ltd
Paddocks Farm, Huish Champflower, Taunton, Somerset, TA4 2HQ
www.verm-x.com
Tel +44 (0) 1984 629 125

VIGO Presses Ltd
Paul Courtney, Unit 4, Flightway, Dunkeswell, Honiton, Devon, EX14 4RD
www.vigopresses.co.uk
Tel +44 (0) 1404 890093

Voran
Voran Maschinen GmbH
Inn 7, A-4632 Pichl bei Wels
Austria
+43 (0)7249 4440
www.voran.at/en/machinery

Voss Electric
P O Box 167, Gloucester, Glos, GL2 8YS
www.electricfencing.co.uk
Tel +44 (0) 1452 346204

Wessex Trailers
Crossways Trailers Ltd T/A Wessex Trailers, Waddock, Cross Dorchester, Dorset, DT2 8QY
www.wessex-trailers.co.uk
Tel +44 (0) 1929 462534

John Worle Ltd
The Orchards, Norton Canon, Hereford, HR4 7BQ
www.johnworle.co.uk
Tel +44 (0) 7769 801394

Insurance providers

Cliverton
15–17 Norwich Road, Fakenham Norfolk, NR21 8AU
www.cliverton.co.uk
Tel +44 (0) 1328 857921

My Farm Insurance
Farm and General Insurance Consultants Ltd, The New Forest Estate Offices, Lyndhurst Road, Brockenhurst, SO42 7RL
www.myfarminsurance.co.uk
Tel +44 (0) 1590 624399

NFU Mutual
Tiddington Road, Stratford Upon Avon, Warwickshire, CV37 7BJ
www.nfumutual.co.uk
Tel +44 (0) 808 274 9563

Rightsure Rural Insurance
Llys Amaeth, Plas Gogerddan, Aberystwyth, SY23 3BT
www.ritesure.co.uk
Tel +44 (0) 1452 223600

Learning providers

Askham Bryan College
Askham Bryan, York, YO23 3FR
www.askham-bryan.ac.uk
Tel +44 (0) 1904 772277

Berkshire College of Agriculture
Hall Place, Burchetts Green, Maidenhead, Berkshire, SL6 6QR
www.bca.ac.uk
Tel +44 (0) 1628 824444

Bishop Burton College
York Road, Bishop Burton,

HU17 8QG
www.bishopburton.ac.uk
Tel +44 (0) 1964 553000

Centre for Alternative Technology
Llwyngwern Quarry, Pantperthog, Machynlleth, SY20 9AZ
www.cat.org.uk/index.html
Tel +44 (0) 1654 705950

Cider and Perry Academy
Mitchell F&D Ltd, 74 Culver Street, Newent, Glos, GL18 1DA
www.cider-academy.co.uk
Tel +44 (0) 1531 828330

Coleg Cambria
Llysfasi, Ruthin Road, Ruthin Denbighshire, LL15 2LB
www.cambria.ac.uk
Tel +44 (0) 300 30 30 007

College of Agriculture, Food and Rural Enterprise
Greenmount Campus, 45 Tirgracy Road, Muckamore, Antrim, Co. Antrim, BT41 4PS Northern Ireland
www.cafre.ac.uk
Tel +44 (0) 28 9442 6601

Duchy College
Rosewarne, Camborne, Cornwall, TR14 0AB
www.duchy.ac.uk
Tel +44 (0) 330 123 4784

Easton and Otley College
Easton, Norwich, Norfolk, NR9 5DX
www.eastonotley.ac.uk
Tel +44 (0) 1603 731200

Hadlow College
Hadlow, Tonbridge, Kent, TN11 0AL
www.hadlow.ac.uk
Tel +44 (0) 1732 850551

Harper Adams University
Newport, Shropshire, TF10 8NB
www.harper-adams.ac.uk
Tel +44 (0) 1952 820280

Hartpury College and University Centre
Hartpury House, Glos, GL19 3BE
www.hartpury.ac.uk
Tel +44 (0) 1452 702244

Kingston Maurward College
Dorchester, Dorset, DT2 8PY
www.kmc.ac.uk
Tel +44 (0) 1305 215000

Lantra
Lantra House, Stoneleigh Park, Stoneleigh, Coventry, Warwickshire, CV8 2LG
www.lantra.co.uk
Tel +44 (0) 2476 696996

Moulton College
West Street, Moulton, Northants, NN3 7RR
www.moulton.ac.uk
Tel +44 (0) 1604 491131

Myerscough College
St Michael's Road, Bilsborrow, Preston, PR3 0RY

www.myerscough.ac.uk
Tel +44 (0) 1995 642222

Plumpton College
Ditchling Road, Plumpton, East Sussex, BN7 3AE
www.plumpton.ac.uk
Tel +44 (0) 1273 890454

Reaseheath College
Nantwich, Cheshire, CW5 6DF
www.reaseheath.ac.uk
Tel +44 (0) 1270 625131

Riseholme College
Riseholme Park, Lincoln, LN2 2LG
www.riseholme.ac.uk
Tel +44 (0) 1522 895490

Royal Agricultural University
Cirencester, Glos, GL7 6JS
www.rau.ac.uk
Tel +44 (0) 1285 652531

Scotland's Rural College
Peter Wilson Building, Kings Buildings, West Mains Road, Edinburgh, EH9 3JG
www.sruc.ac.uk
Tel +44 (0) 800 269 453

Sparsholt College
Westley Lane, Sparsholt, Hampshire, SO21 2NF
www.sparsholt.ac.uk
Tel +44 (0) 1962 776441

Warwickshire College Group
Warwick New Road, Royal Leamington Spa, Warwickshire, CV32 5JE
www.wcg.ac.uk
Tel +44 (0) 300 456 0047

Writtle University College
Lordship Road, Writtle, Chelmsford, Essex, CM1 3RR
www.writtle.ac.uk
Tel +44 (0) 1245 424200

Publications

Country Smallholding Magazine
Archant SW, Unit 3, Old Station Road, Barnstaple, EX32 8PB
www.countrysmallholding.com
Tel +44 (0) 1271 341652

Farmers Guardian
Unit 4, Fulwood Park, Caxton Road, Preston, PR2 9NZ
www.fginsight.com
Tel +44 (0) 1772 799459

Farmers Weekly
Quadrant House, The Quadrant, Sutton, Surrey, SM2 5AS
www.fwi.co.uk
Tel +44 (0) 1208 652 4911

The Good Life Press
https://issuu.com/thegoodlife-press
Tel +44 (0) 1772 633444

Home Farmer Magazine
Firtree, Furnace, Inverary, PA32 8XU

www.homefarmer.co.uk
Tel +44 (0) 1772 633444

Horticulture Week
Haymarket Media Group Ltd
Bridge House, 69 London Road,
Twickenham, TW1 3SP
www.hortweek.com
Tel +44 (0) 20 8267 4277

Permaculture Magazine
The Sustainability Centre,
Droxford Road, East Meon,
Hampshire, GU32 1HR
www.permaculture.co.uk
Tel +44 (0) 1730 823311

Smallholder
Newsquest Media, Falmouth
Business Park, Bickland Water
Road, Falmouth, Cornwall,
TR11 4SZ
www.smallholder.co.uk
Tel +44 (0) 1326 213336

Index

D